'I'm not in lov ... **never will be.'**

But why should th ... accept? After all— ... love with him either. In fact, she couldn't care less if she never saw him again after this weekend.

Could she ... ?

Dear Reader

Christmas is upon us once again, and with Christmas comes the thought of Christmas holidays, Christmas presents, and, of course, romance. This month's selection of books makes wonderful Christmas reading— you can drift away to the exotic Bahamas or imagine yourself having a romantic adventure in Argentina, or in the wilds of Mexico... Whatever your tastes, we know that we have a story that will be just right for you. May you all have a wonderfully romantic Christmas!

The Editor

Sarah Holland was born in Kent and brought up in London. She began writing at eighteen because she loved the warmth and excitement of Mills & Boon. She has travelled the world, living in Hong Kong, the South of France and Holland. She attended a drama school, and was a nightclub singer and a songwriter. She now lives on the Isle of Man. Her hobbies are acting, singing, painting and psychology. She loves buying clothes, noisy dinner parties and being busy.

Recent titles by the same author:

DESERT DESTINY
LAST OF THE GREAT FRENCH LOVERS
RUTHLESS LOVER

CONFRONTATION

BY

SARAH HOLLAND

MILLS & BOON LIMITED
ETON HOUSE   18-24 PARADISE ROAD
RICHMOND   SURREY   TW9 1SR

First published in Great Britain 1992
by Mills & Boon Limited

© *Sarah Holland 1992*

Australian copyright 1992
Philippine copyright 1992
This edition 1992

ISBN 0 263 77833 9

Set in Times Roman 10 on 12 pt.
01-9212-50720 C

Made and printed in Great Britain

CHAPTER ONE

CAROLINE was working overtime again. A quick glance at her watch told her she wasn't going to be late for dinner with Stephen. It was only just gone six, and she would be finished very soon.

Glancing towards her boss's door, she stared at the brass plaque reading: 'MARK RIDER, MANAGING DIRECTOR'. He was an enigma, a hard-faced man with eyes the colour of steel and jet-black hair. She had no idea what went on in his head, but she knew about his private life, and she knew he was an absolute bastard where women were concerned. Common sense told her she ought to dislike him. But when he looked at her...she felt quivers of excitement.

It was like working with an exposed electric cable. Caroline spent her days staring at him, thinking about him, wondering what it would feel like if that electric cable ever made contact with her...

Stop fantasising about him! she chided herself for the hundredth time that day, and got to her feet, pressing 'print' on the computer. The printer began hammering out the letter on expensive paper, the words 'Rider Advertising' in black and red at the top.

The door opened suddenly, and he strode in, devastatingly sexy in his black business suit, a gold watch chain glittering across a taut black waistcoat, his height and muscular build giving him an aura of hard masculinity that made her heart pick up the pace.

Caroline flicked a look at him through her lashes, her green eyes warily excited by him.

'Ah!' His steel-grey eyes flashed over the printer. 'You've finished them all, then?'

'Yes, sir. That's the last one.'

He bent his dark head to study the letter. 'Perfect. I'll sign all copies here and you can get them off.'

Caroline shuffled all the printed letters into a neat pile, took a black and silver pen from the top drawer, and presented them to Mark Rider for his powerful signature.

As he signed, she walked to the other side of the room and took her white coat down, sliding into it, aware of Mark Rider's grey eyes suddenly flicking to her slender curves, softly outlined in the black wool dress.

'You're in quite a hurry,' he drawled softly, a sardonic smile on his cruel mouth. 'I haven't kept you too late, have I?'

'No.' She pulled her long golden brown curls out of the back of the coat, shaking her head automatically as they shimmered like dark spun gold.

The printer came to a halt. Mark glanced at it, whipped the paper out of it, and placed it on the desk, signing in that bold, dynamic way of his.

'I'm rather hungry,' Mark drawled casually, handing the last letter to her and straightening. 'We could have dinner together.'

Caroline tensed, her long lashes flickering, breathless as she studied him with wary green eyes, electricity prickling over her skin.

'Perhaps go to the theatre afterwards,' Mark said under his breath, a tension in his body that increased her excitement.

He had often asked her out for dinner in the last eight months. She had always refused. It was too dangerous for her to spend time in intimate surroundings with him. She knew that instinctively.

'That would be lovely,' Caroline said at last with a slow smile, 'but I'm afraid I have other plans.'

The grey eyes hardened into steel. 'You always do. You must lead a busy life, Miss Shaw.'

'I like to be busy,' she admitted, smiling up at him through her lashes. Then she felt her heart miss a beat, so she quickly lowered her gaze and reached for the letters, leaning over the desk.

The grey eyes moved over her slender body, the white coat open as she leaned over the desk, her slim curves very visible below that black wool dress because it clung to her body so lovingly; her firm breasts were clearly outlined and Mark was studying them with narrowed eyes.

'Seeing your boyfriend tonight?'

She flushed, reached for the neatly typed envelopes. 'Who told you I had a boyfriend?' she joked.

'A young woman with your looks...' he drawled, but his teeth were bared in a dangerous smile, and she knew he was angry that she had refused another invitation from him.

Her flush deepened. 'Thanks for the compliment!' She was putting the letters in the envelopes now, and sealing them one after the other.

'I wonder why you're so cagey, Miss Shaw!' Mark Rider drawled, thrusting his hands into the pockets of that black suit. 'About your private life, I mean. Most secretaries I've employed have been only too happy to chatter endlessly about their boyfriends.'

'Maybe I'm different!' she quipped, shooting him a smile.

'Yes,' he said under his breath. 'I wonder why?'

Suddenly, the crackle of electricity between them flared higher, and Caroline felt her pulses race with it as she straightened, moistening her lips, so deeply aware of him that she wondered how much longer she could go on working with him without the whole situation blowing up in her face.

'I must go,' Caroline said. 'I'll see you tomorrow, sir.'

'Goodnight.' He watched her leave with steely eyes.

As she closed the door she was shaking. Pushing a hand through her gold-brown hair, she exhaled unsteadily, and it wasn't until she left the managing director's suite that she felt the tension ebb away.

Working with that man was like being under threat. She was more sexually aware of him than she had ever been of any man in her life before.

Pressing the lift call button, she thought of his reputation and his women. An absolute bastard, they called him, and they were right. It was cold and dark outside, and she huddled into her coat as she walked to the Tube station. Mark Rider would be driven home by his chauffeur in the back of a long limousine.

He was a very rich man. He had a house in London and a manor in Hampshire. His current girlfriend was a raven-haired fashion model called Venetia Blake. He drove her around at night to expensive London clubs, casinos and restaurants, a powerfully sexy man in a choice of his black Bentley, his black XJS convertible and his black Range Rover.

The gulf between Mark Rider's life and Caroline's was vast, even though she had been born into a wealthy family: all the money was gone now, eaten up by death duties and debts... but the gulf between secretary and boss was always too wide to be crossed by anything but a passing affair, and Caroline was not the type for passing affairs.

She rode home on the crowded train, staring blankly at the adverts above the heads of her fellow passengers. When she got out at her station, it was only a ten-minute walk through the cold London streets to her flat, which was in a large rambling Victorian house in Chiswick.

'I'm just putting the kettle on!' Liz called from the kitchen. 'Do you want some tea?'

'Yes, please!' Caroline closed the door behind her and walked into the narrow little kitchen. 'But I'll just leap into the bath first, so don't hurry!'

'Heavy date with Stephen?'

'Yes, and I've only got an hour to get ready in!' Caroline groaned, nipping into the bathroom and closing the door. Shedding her clothes, she stepped into the bath.

Five minutes later, she emerged, breathless with the speed at which she had bathed. Wrapped in a white towelling robe, her hair in a pink turban made from a small towel, she was squeaky clean and looking forward to her cup of tea.

'You're always doing overtime for that gorgeous boss of yours,' Liz observed, painting her fingernails at the kitchen table. 'Why didn't you tell him you had a big date with Stephen tonight?'

'I knew I could do both if I hurried,' she said evasively.

'You wanted to spend extra time with Mark Rider, you mean!' Liz teased with a smile in her dove-grey eyes as they flicked to Caroline's.

Caroline flushed and said defensively, 'As a matter of fact, he asked me out to dinner again, and I refused.' Laughing, she added, 'So there!'

Liz watched her intently. 'Why do you always refuse?'

Caroline met her eyes and felt a slow, hot flush rise in her face, taking her smile away at once. 'I don't know,' she admitted on a husky note, and looked out of the kitchen window into that familiar midnight-blue darkness, across London's dusty roof-tops, the lights gleaming orange, white, yellow across the city.

Liz frowned. 'He obviously finds you attractive or he wouldn't keep asking you out.'

Caroline felt afraid suddenly, and said, 'I'm sorry, I really have to go and get ready. Stephen will be here in half an hour and my hair's still soaking wet...'

Stephen had stressed the importance of this evening, and had asked her to 'wear something dressy'. When she had blow-dried her hair and put her make-up on, she flicked through her wardrobe. The red dress seemed most appropriate, so she got it out and slid into it.

The doorbell rang. In the hall, she heard Liz answer the door.

'Hi, Stephen.' Liz's voice echoed as she let him in. 'She should be ready. Come in and——'

'I'll be there in a minute!' Caroline called, then hesitated, staring at the strapless red silk that clung to her full, high breasts and tiny waist and the slender curve of her hips. It smoothed down over her long slim thighs and ended just above the knee.

Was it too sexy? Too late now, she thought with a grimace, and snatched up her bag, striding out into the hall.

Stephen caught his breath. 'Darling...you look sensational!'

Caroline smiled, slid into her white coat, and Liz waved them out as they left, their footsteps echoing on the communal stairs that led to the communal hall. There were three other flats housed in the building.

They stepped out into the cold night. Stephen looked young and handsome in a white dinner-jacket and black evening trousers, his dark blond hair brushed back from his pale forehead.

'You're looking awfully smart, Stephen! Where exactly are we going?' Caroline asked him.

'I told you,' he said, a smile on his handsome mouth, 'it's a surprise.' He opened the door of his green saloon car. 'But I guarantee you'll love it, darling. I chose it specially for you.'

Caroline laughed. 'You're very secretive tonight!'

'I have a lot of surprises in store for you!' he smiled, and kissed her mouth before helping her into the front seat, closing the door, then walking round to the driver's door.

They had met six months ago, in the grounds of Chiswick House one Sunday afternoon. Caroline and Liz had been having a picnic on the grass when Stephen's Labrador puppy had come haring over to them, leapt on to their picnic, and started eating it. Stephen had insisted on making amends by taking them both out to dinner. Liz had backed out at the last minute, knowing Stephen really only wanted to be with Caroline.

Tonight, though, Stephen took her to the Ritz.

'Oh, Stephen...!' Caroline was overwhelmed as he led her to the steps of the glittering hotel. 'I can't believe it! This is so——'

'Perfect.' He smiled and kissed her. 'I know. As it's such a special occasion, I decided it was the only place we could come to this evening.'

'Special occasion?' She smiled up at him, the warm breeze in her hair. 'Darling—what on earth is going on? Please tell me.'

'Not yet. Come on.' He offered her his arm, grinning. 'I've booked a table for two for eight o'clock!'

They walked in through that achingly familiar door and into the pale pink and gold luxury of the Ritz. It was breathtakingly beautiful, and the hush of old money made Caroline walk taller. She wondered what was going on in Stephen's mind. Why was this a special occasion? Had he been promoted at work?

'Good evening, sir, madam.' The head waiter of the Palm Court swept up to them in black tails and a charming smile. 'A table for two? May I take your coat, madam?'

As her coat slid from her bare shoulders, she was very glad she had worn this superb red dress, because she felt so totally at home here in it.

They were led to their table across the marble floor. Shaking out her long chestnut-gold curls, Caroline walked with a confident sway in her step, the red dress attracting admiring glances from men as she passed.

Suddenly, she met a pair of steel-grey eyes, saw a hard mouth and felt the crackle of electricity as she stopped dead, staring as her pulse-rate rocketed.

'Good evening, Miss Shaw,' Mark Rider drawled coolly, and his eyes took in the sexy red dress she wore, stripping it slowly from her body...she could almost feel his hand on her zip.

Breathless, she said, 'Good evening, Mr Rider!' and
forced herself to carry on walking, aware of that dark
excitement gripping the pit of her stomach.

'Who was that?' Stephen asked as they sat at their
table in the corner of the marble and gold Palm Court.
'You called him Mr Rider...?'

'My boss,' Caroline confirmed thickly. 'That's Venetia
Blake with him, isn't it? I recognise her from the
magazines...'

Stephen glanced over at them. 'Yes...stunning, isn't
she?'

Caroline's mouth tightened. 'She looks like Countess
Dracula. All that black eyeliner and those red lips!'

'I wouldn't mind feeling her teeth in my neck!' said
Stephen, smiling lazily, then blanched, saying at once,
'God, I'm sorry, Caro! What an oaf I am! Let me order
champagne...'

Later, Caroline and Stephen walked into the elegant
restaurant, dim-lit as the three-piece played Cole Porter,
and waiters in black tails swished about with silver-
domed dishes.

Mark Rider was seated at table one. His narrowed eyes
flicked up as she entered, and moved with steely sexual
appraisal over her body as he leaned back in his seat,
his hard face quite ruthless.

'This is the first time I've ever dined here,' Stephen
confided over the candle-lit table. 'Isn't the ceiling
magnificent?'

Caroline flicked a gaze up at the blue-gold painted
ceiling. 'Yes.' As her gaze slid down it met Mark Rider's
and her heart missed a beat.

Their first course arrived, and they began to eat. The
consommé was light and delicious. The waiters swished

about while the piano, violin and double bass played 'Night and Day'.

The meal was superb. The wild duck was exquisite, served in a elegant strips fanned out on beautiful plates. Afterwards, Caroline chose Ritz sorbets, which arrived with a little crown of spun sugar.

'Well,' Stephen said lightly as their plates were cleared and coffee was ordered, 'it seems the great moment is here and I can't delay any longer.'

Caroline studied him. 'Stephen, you're not being sent away anywhere, are you? You've mentioned promotion before, and——'

'I have been promoted,' he said at once. 'I'm now chief executive salesman!' He ran a hand through his dark blond hair. 'And that brings me neatly to the biggest surprise of all.'

Caroline frowned smilingly, and watched him reach into his inside jacket pocket to pull out a small blue velvet box that made her catch her breath, eyes flashing to his face.

'Darling,' Stephen's voice was husky, 'I realise this is a surprise for you, but you must have known how I felt.'

She was astonished, staring at him, telling herself she loved him, she wanted this to happen . . .

'I love you,' said Stephen, and opened the blue velvet box, reaching slowly across the table to offer it to her. 'And I want you to marry me.' He watched her, and said huskily, 'Please say yes . . .'

Across the restaurant, Mark Rider's dark head slowly turned.

Caroline stared at the diamond solitaire. 'Stephen . . . I don't know what to say.'

'I just told you,' he murmured, flushing. 'Say yes . . .'

She was suddenly powerfully aware of Mark Rider's grey eyes on her, and she was fighting to think coherently. 'Stephen, it's all so sudden!'

He watched her face. 'You know I'm desperately in love with you. I've told you often enough...'

'I know, but...' Caroline studied him, wanting to accept, yet wanting to be fair to him, and wanting most of all for Mark Rider to stop looking at her.

'You can have time to think it over.' Stephen was watching her face intently. 'How long do you need?'

Caroline flicked her gaze to his face. 'I don't need time to think it over,' she said with a warm smile. 'Stephen, of course I'll marry you!'

'Oh, God...!' His eyes flared with joy, and he took the ring from the velvet box, sliding it on to her finger. 'I'm so happy, darling...'

A couple started dancing cheek to cheek in the dimly lit restaurant, close to the piano.

'Shall we celebrate with a dance?' Stephen was beaming at her, and she smiled, nodding. He rose to his feet, handsome in his white dinner-jacket and black trousers, and led her to the small dance area on the plush carpet close to the grand piano, the violinist and the palm tree.

Caroline rested her head on his shoulder as he held her in his arms.

'I'd like to set a date for the wedding as soon as possible,' Stephen told her huskily, holding her tight. 'Can we talk about it?'

Something in her tensed. 'I'll need time to think about a wedding, Stephen,' she said with gentle sincerity. 'Don't make any public announcements. It's all happening awfully fast, and I'm not truthfully a hundred per cent sure about it . . .'

'All right.' He kissed her mouth softly, smiling. 'I'll give you all the time you need.'

The music stopped. Hand in hand they returned to their table. A second later, Mark Rider was getting to his feet, and with a shock she realised he was walking over to her.

'Miss Shaw.' Mark reached their table, hands in the trouser pockets of his magnificent black evening suit. 'I realise this is hardly the office party, but nevertheless I feel I must ask you to dance.'

Caroline's eyes widened with shock, but she had no real choice other than to accept with a wary smile, standing up, feeling those steel-grey eyes rove like fire over her sensual body.

Mark flicked a cynical smile at Stephen. 'You don't mind, Mr . . . ?'

'Daly.' Stephen got to his feet, extending a hand. 'Stephen Daly.'

'How do you do?' Mark drawled, flicking a mocking look at Caroline as he shook Stephen's hand. 'Do excuse us . . .' His hard hand slid to the small of Caroline's back, propelling her inexorably towards the small dance area close to the piano.

He turned her as they reached it, and his strong hands slid slowly on to her waist, raising prickles of excitement in her as she looked up at his hard face and felt her mouth go dry.

'Well, Miss Shaw!' Mark drawled softly. 'It seems you can't keep secrets all the time!'

She flushed hotly. 'Stephen wasn't a secret!'

'Of course not,' his voice said above her head. 'And I'm sure you would have told me all about your engagement first thing in the morning!'

Caroline looked up at him angrily. 'I would have worn the ring!'

'And avoided all my questions,' he said, his mouth moving in a hard smile. 'But at least now I know why you've refused all my invitations. I take it you've been seeing him for a year or so?'

'No,' she said, avoiding his eyes. 'Six months.'

His body tensed and she could sense his anger as he drawled tightly, 'Just six months? So you met him after you came to work for me?'

'Yes,' she said, dry-mouthed.

Those strong hands were on her waist, and they were tighter now, as Caroline rested unsteady hands on his chest and felt his heart beat with rage.

'That's a lovely dress, Miss Shaw,' Mark said softly, an edge of steel in his voice as he looked down at her through carved lids. 'It makes you look quite unbearably sexy. What does your fiancé do?'

'He's chief executive salesman for Baker Plastics,' she said hotly.

'A plastics man!' he drawled tightly. 'When's the wedding?'

Her face flamed. 'We haven't set a date yet. I'll need time to think about it. Marriage is such a very big step.'

'Marriage is for fools!' he said in a voice like steel, and then he met her gaze and gave a slow cynical smile, drawling, 'Forgive me, Miss Shaw! Just a personal opinion!'

'An opinion I don't share,' she said flatly, 'or I wouldn't be marrying Stephen.'

'Well, I thought you weren't marrying him,' he drawled. 'I understood there was some problem. Something you needed time to think about...?'

Defiantly, she lifted her chin. 'I've only been seeing him for six months! I can't just marry him without thinking about it! After all—six months isn't very long.'

'It is if you want to go to bed with someone,' he said, eyes like knives as he looked directly into hers, and she felt breathless, aware of the anger in him, and the accusation.

'Stephen isn't like that!' she snapped. 'Neither am I!' Then caught her breath in horror, whispering, 'I mean——'

'I know what you meant, Miss Shaw,' Mark drawled mockingly, and then the music stopped. He led her back to her table, a hard smile on his mouth. He exchanged a polite sentence with Stephen, then strode back to Venetia Blake, who was glaring at them.

Caroline felt shaken, disturbed, angry. She said to Stephen, 'Shall we go? It's late and we both have to go to work tomorrow morning...'

They drove home in Stephen's saloon. He parked under the tree outside her flat, and turned to her, drawing her into his embrace and sighing into her cloud of dark gold hair. His kiss was warm and gentle, almost childlike, and Caroline received it patiently until he was ready to release her.

'Wait.' He held her as she tried to leave. 'About this weekend. I wanted to ask you earlier, but I just forgot. My parents want to meet you. I thought we could drive down there on Saturday?'

Caroline paused, studying him. 'Of course I'll come, Stephen.'

'We'll have to stay the night, of course,' he warned. 'In separate bedrooms, naturally, but York is a long drive, and we'd be exhausted if we tried to do it there and back in a day.'

Caroline smiled. 'Thank your parents very much for the invitation, and tell them I'll be delighted to come.'

'It'll be like giving you a new family,' he said, stroking her hair tenderly.

'That's very sweet of you, and I'm sure it will eventually be true,' she said, 'but my own family were wonderful. Even if they are all gone now. And I only ever had my parents, Stephen. No siblings—remember?'

'Not even a cousin,' he said sadly. 'Poor Caroline.'

'No sympathy, darling. Fate deals the cards and we just make the best of them.'

'It must have been a terrible shock, though, when they were killed in that car crash.'

She sighed and nodded. 'It was. But that was three years ago, Stephen, and I've come to terms with it.'

'Still, it will be nice to give you a second family. And I'm sure you'll get on well with mine, darling. They're so looking forward to meeting you, and they're really very nice people.'

'They must be,' she said, smiling. 'You're their son.'

But later, as she let herself into her flat, she felt intolerably confused. Everything seemed to be happening so quickly. Stephen had obviously saved all this up in order to wait and see if she accepted his proposal, and, although she could understand that, she couldn't quite take it all in.

Looking at her engagement ring, she felt a sudden pang of anxiety. If she was in love with Stephen, why had she spent the entire evening unable to take her mind and eyes off Mark Rider?

And why did he make her feel so excited...so afraid...?

CHAPTER TWO

NEXT morning, Caroline arrived at the office feeling
tense with apprehension. Mark's behaviour last night had
alarmed her. He had always probed for personal information with her, but he had never been quite so direct.

Caroline didn't like giving out personal information
about herself. It made her feel vulnerable and ill at ease.
At boarding-school, confessing secrets to the other girls
had been dangerous. Teenage girls habitually made and
broke friendships at the drop of a hat. Whenever
Caroline had confided personal secrets to friends, they
had eventually been spread all over the school with ma-
licious giggling behind hands. In the end, she had simply
stopped confiding in people. She had never confided in
her parents—they were just never around. Besides, they
weren't really interested in her life, and any confidences
would have been indifferently received.

Hanging up her coat, she smoothed down the smart
black skirt suit she wore. It outlined her figure, but was
severe, starkly classical, and her hair shimmered against
its velvet black lines.

She went to her desk and sorted through the mail. The
intercom buzzed. Blinking at it, Caroline felt her pulses
race, and leaned forward to depress the key.

'Yes, sir?' Her voice was cool, remote, professional.

'Come through, Miss Shaw,' Mark said softly, and
there was a thread of menace in his voice that made her
heart miss a beat. Going into his office, she saw him

seated at his desk, relaxing with his hands behind his dark head as he watched her, his eyes moving in leisurely inspection of her slender shape.

'The mail, sir,' Caroline said coolly, walking across the deep-pile cream carpet and placing the envelopes on his vast mahogany desk.

He smiled like a lazy tiger, flicked his grey eyes to her face and said softly, 'Sit down, Miss Shaw.'

Caroline moved to the chair opposite him, sank down on it, watching his tough face through her lashes. He wore one of his expensive grey suits today. It was impeccably cut, as all his clothes were, and the taut waistcoat gleamed with a gold watch-chain. White cuffs accentuated his tan as they peeped out from beneath grey sleeves. The dark red silk tie was coolly knotted at his strong throat. He looked irresistible, sexy, powerful, self-assured . . . and very dangerous.

'I'm afraid something's come up,' Mark said coolly. 'Jack Rachey is trying to pull out of the deal I set up for him last month. I got a fax through from Rachey Cosmetics, ten minutes ago.' He handed her a print-out. 'It's a delay on signing the contract.'

Caroline studied the fax with a frown. Rachey were one of the biggest cosmetics manufacturers in Europe. They held the cheapest end of the market, selling good cosmetics at very low prices.

'I want to keep the Rachey account,' Mark said flatly.

'I can't believe he's trying to pull out.' Caroline lifted her head, still frowning. 'He was so enthusiastic. And he loved the art-work and story-boarding. What on earth can have made him change his mind?'

'Fear of the unknown?' Mark arched black brows. 'Jeffers and Jeffers have had the Rachey account for ten years.'

'But they've grown stale lately.'

'Right,' his hard voice agreed. 'And that's why he came to us. A fresh look at an old product.'

'What are you going to do?' she asked.

'I'm going to go and get his signature on that damned contract,' he drawled. 'What do you think?'

'Next week?' she asked, pen poised over her pad. 'Shall I make an appointment with——?'

'No,' he said flatly. 'It'll have to be done immediately. Cancel all my appointments from eleven o'clock this morning.'

'Right.' Caroline jotted that down on her notepad.

'We'll go home and pack a few clothes,' he said softly, watching her face, 'then drive to Cornwall. We should get there at about——'

Slowly, she had lifted her head, meeting the thrust of his steel eyes. 'We?' she asked carefully. 'Did you say we . . . ?'

'Well, of course,' he murmured, watching her intently. 'I'm going to need you with me on this one, Miss Shaw. You've worked closely on the account from the word go. Nobody knows all the details as well as you.'

'But . . .' she could barely stop staring into his tough face ' . . . but Mr Rider, I can't go to Cornwall with you!'

'This is an emergency, Miss Shaw.' His eyes narrowed, his voice hardening with implicit threat. 'I must insist you accompany me.'

'Sir, it's just not possible!' Her mouth was faintly dry. 'Apart from anything, I don't really see why you need me with you at all, and——'

'You know everything about the account from A to Z,' he told her in a tough voice. 'You're practically my personal assistant, and Jack Rachey took a fancy to you the minute he met you.'

Her lashes flickered. 'You're asking me to come along as a hired flirt?'

'Why not?' he drawled with an edge to his voice. 'You're good at it.'

Annoyance sparkled in her eyes. 'What do you mean, good at it?'

'Promising everything. Giving nothing.' His eyes were narrowed and his mouth hard. 'Isn't that the art of flirtation, Miss Shaw?'

She stared tensely, aware of the steel in his voice. That was a very personal and knife-edged comment for a girl to get from her boss. But this was no ordinary boss, and theirs was no ordinary working relationship. They had both been aware of that from the outset. Now Mark Rider was forcing it out into the open.

'At any rate,' Mark said coolly, 'I need you with me. Can you be ready to leave by midday?'

Carefully she asked, 'Jack Rachey lives in Cornwall, doesn't he?'

He inclined his dark head, watching her with a hard smile.

'So we would only have to be away for one day?'

'Oh, no,' he said softly. 'We'd have to stay at least until Sunday.'

'Then I can't come,' Caroline said in a cool, professional voice. 'I've already made arrangements for the weekend and I can't possibly cancel them.'

'What arrangements?' he asked in a hard voice.

'Stephen is taking me to York tomorrow to meet his family.'

The air suddenly seemed to vibrate with an under-current of violence as Mark looked at her, his face very hard. 'So he's taking you home to meet his family, is he?' His mouth hardened. 'How very tedious of him. I suppose you're looking forward to taking tea with his mother while she shows you the baby photographs!'

Her eyes flashed. 'You're being insulting, Mr Rider!'

'And you're being very unprofessional,' he drawled. 'I don't pay you to do what you want, Miss Shaw, but what I want. This is an important business weekend and I insist you accompany me.'

'But surely you can see it's impossible?' she said angrily. 'This isn't an ordinary weekend for me. I've just got engaged to this man. I've agreed to meet his family. It would be unforgivable of me to let him down at the last——'

'Would you prefer to be fired?' he cut in flatly.

The threat took her breath away. Fury shot through her, turning her eyes a very fierce green. 'You'll fire me,' she asked in a tightly controlled voice, 'if I refuse to accompany you to Cornwall?'

He smiled slowly, eyes mocking. 'It is stated clearly in your contract that you must accompany me on any business trip, regardless of circumstance, even if it is at the drop of a hat.'

'Yes, but this is grossly unfair!' she said furiously. 'You know perfectly well that my recent engagement puts a very different light on the terms of that contract.'

He laughed softly, enjoying her rage. 'Are you raising your voice to me, Miss Shaw?'

Her mouth tightened. She struggled to control herself. 'I'll have to ring Stephen and tell him I can't go. What do you suppose he'll think? What would you think in his position?'

'That you were backing out,' he drawled with open mockery.

'Is that why you're insisting I come with you?' The question shot out before she could stop herself.

His smile taunted her. 'Now would I do such a thing?'

'Yes,' she said tightly, 'I believe you would.'

Mark laughed softly. 'Are you accusing me of deliberately trying to put a spanner in the works?'

'Yes!'

'Come now, Miss Shaw,' he drawled, 'you're being unprofessional again. I realise this is an inconvenient time for a business trip, but such is life. You signed that contract, you get all the benefits—and now you're coming face to face with the drawbacks.' His brows arched. 'This is one of them. Just accept it. Cancel your weekend with the plastics man and come to Cornwall with me.'

Caroline looked at him with loathing. 'Kindly stop referring to my fiancé as "the plastics man".'

'But that's what he is.'

'I'll start calling you the advertising man, then, shall I?' she snapped.

'You'll call me sir,' he said softly, 'or I'll teach you a lesson you won't forget.'

Her breath caught. The statement had a ring of sexual threat, as did his eyes, his ruthless mouth and his smoky voice. Caroline had no doubt whatever that he was capable of carrying it out and a throb of excitement leapt in her body at the thought of it.

Drawing an unsteady breath, she said with a flash of anger in her eyes, 'When do you need my answer?'

'Within the next hour,' he said flatly, and glanced at his watch, crisp white cuffs shooting back to expose the tanned skin and hair-roughened wrist. 'It's just gone nine. We'd have to leave here at eleven, fling some clothes into a couple of cases, and be on our way to Cornwall by midday. I've already arranged dinner tonight with Rachey.'

This was a nightmare, but she had to go through with it, although her voice was tight with open rage. 'Where would we be staying?'

'At a hotel,' he said coolly, and smiled cynically, adding, 'Separate rooms, of course.'

'I wouldn't even consider it without separate rooms,' she snapped, hating him.

He gave a cynical smile. 'Good. I'd hate to think you were an easy conquest.'

Caroline leapt to her feet with a burst of fury. 'How dare you?' She threw her pen and pad on to the desk, shaking. 'My God, if you seriously think I'm coming to——'

'Temper, temper!' he drawled, laughing, and got to his feet, striding around the desk to her, towering over her with a gleam of mockery in his eyes. 'And I thought you were such a cool, calm young lady.'

Heart leaping, she struggled for self-control. 'What did you mean by that remark?' she demanded, breathing erratically. 'Is this really a business trip, or——?'

'It's a business trip,' he drawled mockingly. 'And my remark was a piece of male chauvinism.'

She breathed easier, but her heart was still thumping. 'Badly chosen words, Mr Rider. It sounded very much as though you had an ulterior motive for this trip that has nothing to do with Rachey Cosmetics.'

The grey eyes were penetrating. 'Now why should you think that?' he asked under his breath.

Wary excitement stirred in her. She watched him through her lashes, silent.

'After all,' he said with a slow, dangerous smile, 'you've made it more than clear that you wouldn't be interested in a more personal relationship with me.'

Her lashes flickered. Slowly, her eyes moved to that ruthless mouth and a quiver of excitement went through her.

'You've refused countless invitations,' he said under his breath, his powerful body very close to hers, 'and given no indication that you find me attractive.'

Her eyes shot to his face, desire blazing in them.

He met her gaze with equal sexual excitement. 'Have you, Miss Shaw?' he asked softly, accusingly, unsmilingly.

She was breathless. She couldn't reply. The electricity between them was intolerable. They both knew it. Shivers ran through her at the thought of what would happen if they ever kissed.

'You have fifty-five minutes to make up your mind about this trip to Cornwall,' Mark Rider said under his breath. 'I suggest you use them wisely.'

'I'll be in my office,' she said, her voice husky, and he gave a cool nod, eyes narrowing as he watched her walk out of the luxurious office and back into her own.

As she closed the door, she felt the tingles of electricity run over her skin and looked down at her hands to find them shaking. Drawing an unsteady breath, she walked to her desk.

I find him frighteningly attractive, she thought, eyes closing briefly. And he knows it. But he's a complete bastard where women are concerned—and I'm not letting him anywhere near me.

So now what was she supposed to do? She couldn't afford to lose this job. Her rent was bad enough, but the expenses of electricity, food, petrol—if she lost just one month's wages through being fired, the whole thing would collapse.

It was intolerable even to consider what life would be like if she was fired. She couldn't ask Stephen to support her, and Liz didn't earn enough to lend her more than enough to buy a hamburger. Her parents had been dead for years, and she had no other relatives.

Just the thought of spending a weekend with Mark Rider in a hotel was enough to make her shake with nerves, but she pushed that Achilles heel away from her, refusing to dwell on the deep channel that buzzed continually between her and her disturbing boss.

Picking up the phone, she punched out Stephen's office number.

'Extension seventeen,' she clipped out coolly to the receptionist, and a moment later the line rang and Stephen answered it.

Quickly, Caroline outlined the details of her conversation with Mark, taking great care to omit the way he'd looked at her, and the way she always responded to those penetrating grey eyes as they moved over her body.

'I can't believe he'd threaten you with the sack!' Stephen said incredulously. 'It's just so callous of him!'

'He knows I need this job,' she said tightly.

'But surely it would be unfair dismissal?'

'Unfortunately, no.' Caroline made a wry face. 'My contract does stipulate that business trips will occasionally be required of me and that refusal to comply could lead to dismissal.'

'But you've been there for eight months, and this is the first trip he's demanded,' Stephen said.

'Presumably, it's the first emergency.' Caroline gave a pained sigh. 'I remember being over the moon about the salary he was paying me. Now I can see why I'm paid so well.'

'Because you're expected to drop everything at a moment's notice and rush off to talk to a jittery client,' Stephen agreed sadly. 'Yes, I suppose his demands are reasonable, looked at in that light.'

'Yes...' Caroline frowned a little. 'Maybe I've reacted badly to this. I was—well, a little rude to him.'

'Were you?' Stephen laughed. 'How did you dare, Caroline? He's one of the most ruthless-looking sharks I've ever met!'

'He's a complete bastard!' Caroline said thickly, gripping the phone with white knuckles. 'I certainly don't envy any of his women! I can just imagine how he treats them!'

Her heart leapt a little with fear and excitement: she was facing a weekend alone with the electric cable. What would it be like to be with him for a weekend under such intimate circumstances?

Stephen was obviously thinking the same thing. 'I hope it is just business, Caro,' he said suddenly. 'A weekend alone with him——'

'Of course it's just business!' she reassured him huskily. 'Mark Rider definitely doesn't—want anything from me. It's a genuine business trip, and I'll be back on Sunday to reassure you of that.'

Later, when Caroline had said goodbye to him, she sat for a moment and thought about their conversation. So she wasn't the only one who was aware of Mark's powerful sexual interest in her.

Getting to her feet, she went to his office and knocked calmly on the door.

'Come in!' he drawled coolly, and she opened the door to find him surrounded by paperwork, his jacket off, his tie loosened at the throat as he worked at his desk.

Caroline raised her gold-brown head, face haughty. 'I've telephoned my fiancé to cancel my weekend plans. I will be accompanying you to Cornwall.'

He studied her for a second, then his mouth moved in a cool, cynical smile. 'Good,' he said softly. 'Leave here at eleven, go home and pack. I'll pick you up at midday from your flat.'

'My address is——'

'I know your address, Caroline,' he murmured, and the use of her Christian name sent a quiver through her as he leaned back and let his grey eyes drift insolently over her body right down to her slim ankles and high black heels.

Caroline gave a curt nod, and left the office. Her skin was prickling all over. She leant on the door, listening to her thudding heartbeat.

He's going to try to kiss me once we get to Cornwall, she thought, and her pulses clamoured violently at the thought of that hard, ruthless mouth on hers. Fury shot through her. He can try all he likes! I won't be used to satisfy his sexual curiosity about me, and there's an end to it.

The flat was strangely silent as she let herself in. It was also freezing cold. She shivered, went to her bedroom and packed a small suitcase, selecting various clothes, a nightdress, silky lingerie and two reliable day dresses.

At midday, a black Bentley turbo drove up outside, and her pulses leapt as she stared down at it, heard the discreet throb of power as Mark guided it skilfully to a standstill and switched off the engine.

She went downstairs with her suitcase. As she opened the door, he was walking coolly up the path. His black hair flickered around his tanned forehead.

He was wearing a black cashmere coat over that grey business suit. 'Ready?' he mocked softly, and she shivered as she heard the unspoken question in his voice, and knew deep inside that there was far more to this weekend than met the eye.

But she couldn't say it. So she just nodded, and clipped out, 'Yes!'

He smiled lazily, his grey eyes slid to her mouth, and then he took her case, walked with her to the car, and stowed it in the capacious boot before striding round to the driver's side.

Caroline breathed in the scent of the expensive upholstery, waiting for him in the passenger-seat, and when he slid in beside her she felt her pulses hammer like wildfire, watching him through her lashes.

The engine flared and they drove away.

'How did Stephen take it?' Mark drawled coolly as they sped on to the M4 via the Chiswick roundabout.

'He wasn't pleased,' she said, brows lifting.

'And his parents?'

'Luckily, he hadn't confirmed the arrangement with them.'

Mark nodded. 'So he didn't end up looking a fool in front of them. That's good.'

She said on an angry impulse, 'Well, Mr Rider, you surprise me! You're not completely callous, after all!'

'Not completely,' he drawled, laughing under his breath, and the car shot out of London at an incredible speed as Mark relaxed at the wheel, one strong hand resting on the console beside her, making her very aware of those long fingers.

They drove in silence for a while.

Suddenly, Mark said, 'Thought about a wedding date yet?'

Her face grew haughty. 'I haven't really had time...'

'A woman in love doesn't need time,' he told her tightly. 'She just needs the dress, the church and the honeymoon.'

'I think you're being rather too black and white about it,' she said defensively. 'There's a lot more than that to be taken into account with a wedding.'

'Such as?'

'Well...' She racked her brains, aware he was trying to make it look as though she did not want to marry Stephen. 'Trying to arrange our schedules to fit together, trying to——'

'Comparing Filofaxes!' he mocked. 'How romantic!'

'You're just being unkind, Mr Rider!' she said tightly. 'And——'

'You'll have to stop calling me Mr Rider,' he said with a frown. 'My name is Mark.'

She looked through her lashes at him. 'I thought I was to call you sir—or you'd teach me a lesson.'

He laughed softly, glancing at her through those hooded eyelids. 'I was referring to office politics. But we're not in the office any more. Are we? So new game rules apply.'

'Is this a game, then?' she asked tightly.

'Just call me Mark, and we'll get along much better.'

Caroline felt a tremor go through her and looked away. 'I can't possibly call you Mark. I'm your secretary. You're my boss. It wouldn't be appropriate.'

'We've known each other for eight months. I'm not a stranger to you.' He flicked her a cool look, asked, 'Do you think of me as Mr Rider?'

Caroline studied him through her lashes. 'I don't understand...'

'When you think of me,' he enunciated coolly, looking back at the road, 'do you think of me as Mr Rider or Mark?'

She moistened her lips, hesitating.

'Don't tell me you think of me as "sir"!' he drawled with mockery in his steel eyes. 'Or I'll stop the car and kiss the life out of you, little Miss Shaw!'

Hot colour flooded her face and she caught her breath audibly, staring at him, her lips parted and her heart drumming with sudden violence.

Mark smiled slowly at the look on her face. 'And that's something we both know I've wanted to do for a long time,' he said softly, 'so don't tempt me.'

Caroline couldn't speak for a moment. It was true and they both knew it and the electricity flashing between them in the car made her breasts ache suddenly as her nipples erected and she had to look away from him, her heart drumming.

She said in a constricted voice, 'I think of you as Mark.'

His lashes flickered. 'Good.'

He was demanding personal talk. She felt as though she was in danger and stared out of the window, wishing she could turn this powerful Bentley around and go straight home.

'So,' Mark drawled a moment later, 'tell me how you met Stephen.'

Her head turned. 'How I met him...?'

'We've got a long drive ahead of us,' he said coolly. 'We've got to talk about something.'

'We could try talking about the Rachey account!' she said through stiff lips. 'That is, after all, what we're here for, isn't it? To settle some unfinished business?'

'Oh, we're here to settle unfinished business, all right!' he said tightly, and the look he shot her through his carved lids took her breath away.

'I'm talking about the Rachey account,' she said through dry lips.

'We'll settle all unfinished business, Miss Shaw,' he said softly, 'when we reach our hotel!'

Her mouth trembled and she said thickly, 'Turn this car around at once! I want to go back to London.'

'Don't give me orders, Caroline,' he said with steel mockery. 'I rather think that's my job—don't you?'

'Only in a professional capacity!'

'We'll soon see about that,' he said softly and shot her a cool look. A smile curved his hard mouth and he laughed at her shocked expression, then drawled, 'Tell me about Stephen. You said you met him six months ago...?'

Caroline's lips tightened. 'I don't want to discuss it with you!'

'I know.' His smile was lazy. 'But I'm your boss and I'm driving this car, and you, Caroline, will do as I say!'

She felt rage flood her, burst out angrily, 'Stephen was right! You are a ruthless shark!'

'Oh, yes?' he said, eyes narrowing. 'What else did he say?'

'That you——' she began angrily, and then broke off, biting her lip and looking away. It would hardly be a good idea to tell him Stephen thought he fancied her.

'Mmm?' He flicked a sardonic look at her. 'Carry on. I'm all ears.'

Her lips tightened. 'It doesn't matter!'

He laughed softly. 'Don't worry. I think I can guess.' He looked back at the road, eyes narrowed. 'So how did you meet him?'

'You're not going to give up, are you?' Caroline snapped thickly.

'You catch on fast,' he drawled mockingly.

Her mouth tightened. 'I met Stephen one Sunday afternoon in the grounds of Chiswick House...' she found herself saying, and told him the story of Stephen's Labrador eating the picnic.

'And he took you out to dinner,' Mark guessed, eyes narrowed.

'Yes,' she said in surprise.

'Did he kiss you?'

Anger flooded her veins. 'Mr Rider, you're being personal again!'

'And you're being deliberately impersonal,' he said tightly. 'Now, call me Mark, or I'll pull over and make you.'

She swallowed, mouth tight with anger. 'All right, then—Mark!'

'So obedient!' he mocked, laughing at her. 'And you're right, I'm being personal. Accept it and answer my question. Did Stephen kiss you on your first date?'

'No!' she said angrily, green eyes flaring. 'I wouldn't let him! Does that satisfy you?'

'Oh, very much so!' he murmured. 'When exactly did he kiss you?'

'On our third date, if you must know!'

'You held him off that long?' His brows rose. 'You're a smooth operator, aren't you? It can't have been easy. When did he first try to take you to bed?'

'My God!' she erupted furiously, fire flashing from her eyes. 'You insolent bast——'

'Let me give you a word of advice, Caroline!' he drawled tightly. 'Never call me insolent unless you want to provoke a little more than a kiss out of me.' He studied her angry face and laughed under his breath. 'It makes me want to show you just how insolent I can be. Got that?'

Her body tingled with that fearful excitement again, and she looked away, saying thickly, 'Got it.'

'Good girl,' Mark said, mouth hard. 'Now carry on with the story. When did he first try to take you to bed?'

'Stop it!' she exploded, hatred flashing from her eyes. 'You already know too much about me! I can't stand you knowing anything about me! Anything at all! I can't even stand you near me! I can't stand the way you look at me, the way you make me feel, the way——' She broke off, appalled, a look of horror in her eyes.

His black lashes flickered. He sent her a deadly grey look and the expression in those silver eyes made her heart miss several beats.

'Well,' he said under his breath, 'that just about tells me everything I need to know. Doesn't it, Caroline?'

Caroline looked away. She felt as though she'd been staked stark naked to an ant-hill: exposed suddenly, vulnerable and defenceless, and she bitterly regretted coming on this trip.

He was going to make that advance on her, that advance she had been preventing for eight long months, and suddenly she didn't believe she would be able to hold him off.

CHAPTER THREE

THE hotel was perched high on a cliff like a red stone eagle's nest. Mark guided the Bentley smoothly through the red stone gates, up a tree-lined sloping drive, and parked outside it smoothly.

'Two suites,' Mark drawled, cynical eyes inspecting the inviting mouth of the blonde receptionist. 'Mr Rider and Miss Shaw. They were booked in my name, with this.' He handed her his gold card.

'Yes, sir.' The blonde cast admiring glances at him through her lashes, and turned to get the registration forms.

Caroline deliberately walked away, her body filled with intolerable tension. At least he had kept his word and booked separate rooms.

They rode up in the lift together, tension crackling between them. 'Here's your key,' Mark said, handing it to her, his face hard. 'Rest and relax for the next hour. I'll give you a call.'

The lift doors opened, allowing her to escape the tension. She half expected him to follow her and give her what he was so obviously promising her on this trip. But he went to the door of the suite next to hers, and went inside, closing the door behind him with a quiet click.

Unlocking the door, she went inside, followed by the porter, who deposited her case, accepted a small tip, and left.

It was a beautiful suite, with rich cream carpets, pale green couch and armchairs, a glass and gold coffee-table, and very spacious living area. Wide windows lead to a balcony, the curtains were floor-length and very expensive, and the bedroom was superb, with a vast king-sized bed and mirrored wardrobes.

Resolving not to think about Mark, Caroline went into the bathroom and luxuriated in a long scented bath. Later, she padded into the living-room in a white towelling robe and blow-dried her hair, then changed into her evening clothes.

The black dress was slim-fitting, strapless, hugging her high, firm breasts and nipping in at her slender waist and slim hips. Brushing out her long gold-brown hair, she added make-up, scent and discreet jewellery.

Then she rang room service and ordered a pot of coffee.

Studying the phone, she wondered if she could call Stephen and put his mind at rest. Resolving to pay for the call herself at the end of the trip, she dialled Stephen's home number.

'Hello, darling!' she said with a smile when he answered, and began talking, telling him what the hotel was like, and reassuring him of her safety.

When the knock came on the door, she said, 'Hang on. My coffee's arrived!' and left the phone on the sofa as she went to answer the door.

She had a shock when she met Mark's steel-grey eyes.

'Who are you on the phone to?' he demanded. 'I've been trying to call you.'

Crimsoning, she said, 'It's Stephen. I thought I'd better ring and let him know——'

'That you're safe?' His cynical mouth hardened. 'Well,
I think I'll just assure him that you're not going to be
safe for very much longer!' He pushed open the door,
striding past her, magnificent in a black business suit
with a dark red silk tie, and she could see he had
showered too, his hair freshly dried, his jaw clean-shaven.

'No!' Caroline raced after him, letting the door slam.

Mark picked up the phone, steely mockery in his eyes.
'Daly? This is Mark Rider. I'm just about to——'

'Shut up!' she hissed, snatching the phone from him,
her eyes blazing. 'Stephen? Yes…take no notice of him.'

Mark laughed derisively, watching her with a lazy
smile.

'All right, darling,' Stephen's voice said from a long
way away. 'But tell me you love me before you go. I miss
you so much…'

'Get off the phone!' Mark drawled loudly, listening,
his head close to the earpiece.

'Stephen—I'll call you tomorrow. Yes…bye!' Putting
the phone down, she looked angrily into Mark's eyes.

'Very romantic!' he mocked. 'Why didn't you tell him
you loved him?'

Her face flamed. 'Shut up!'

He laughed. 'Most women seem to litter their conversations with the bloody phrase *ad nauseam*.' His eyes
were cynical. 'Thought about the wedding date yet?'

'Look—this is none of your business!' she snapped.
'We're supposed to be discussing Rachey Cosmetics!'

'I don't want to discuss Rachey Cosmetics,' he
drawled, and caught her wrist, pulling her without
warning on to the sofa, on to his lap, as she gave a hot
gasp, heart drumming, and her hands clutched at his
broad shoulders.

There was a long, intense silence. They stared at each other. Her hair was a soft cloud of silk around her face. She looked at him with hot green eyes through strands of it, her pulses thudding fast.

'Let me go, Mark...' she whispered, bitterly aware of his hard thighs against hers and of his tough face above her.

'No,' he said softly, his eyes staring into hers like fragmented steel. 'I've wanted to kiss your brains out for eight months. This is the first chance I've had and I'm taking it!'

She tried to get away from him. 'No...!'

He caught her easily, his hands hard on her waist as he dragged her back. 'I can't help my feelings, Caroline,' he said under his breath. 'Any more than you can.'

'I don't know what you're talking about!' she said fiercely, heart drumming as she placed her hands on his chest and felt, incredibly, the hard thud of his heart.

'Yes, you do,' he said thickly, grey eyes penetrating. 'I wanted you the minute I laid eyes on you, and you wanted me too. This is mutual, Caroline. I can feel it.' His strong hand slid swiftly to her throat, touching the pulse that throbbed violently there as he tilted her back on his lap, his dark head hovering over hers like a bird of prey as he whispered, 'I can feel it in your blood...give me your hand and feel that pulse!' His eyes darkened like black, bottomless wells as he said thickly, 'And then feel my pulses! Every last one of them...'

'No, Mark!' she protested hoarsely, staring up at him as he slid her down, his hard hands implacable and his eyes narrowed hungrily on her mouth. 'I'll fight you...!'

'You've been fighting me for months!' he bit out under his breath. 'I've tried every trick in the book to get you alone. Dinner invitations, party invitations, overtime...'

Caroline felt her blood begin to throb, her hair sliding like silk over his hard forearm as he closed in on her. 'Mark, don't...'

'But you just keep me at arm's length, don't you?' The grey eyes seemed to splinter. 'You look at me and my temperature rockets, but when I ask for a date, you give me that wary look and back away from me!' His voice thickened. 'You're driving me mad, you little bitch! I know you want me...but you won't let me near you...'

'Stop it!' she said on a fierce whisper, her mouth shaking as his head came closer until their mouths were almost touching, and her heart was going like a rocket.

'But now I've got you alone,' he whispered thickly, 'and I'm going to make you admit the way you feel. Even if I have to drive you insane with rage to do it...' His hard mouth closed over hers with a slow, sensual kiss that made her moan from deep in the back of her throat, her mouth opening instinctively beneath his in a moment of pure unadulterated desire. Then she realised what she was doing, and panic shot through her like fire.

'No...!' she cried hoarsely, jerking her mouth from his, and suddenly she was fighting him, her breath coming rapidly as she struggled to sit up, raining blows on his broad shoulders, but he just kept her steady and took her wrists, then started pushing her backwards into the cushions, and swung his legs on to the couch until she lay trapped beneath his hard body.

Helpless, dazed, she stared up into his dangerous face and her heart was slamming as she felt his hard thighs on hers, felt him slowly slide one between hers, making her mouth open with quivering, defenceless desire and her eyes glaze as she stared at his hard mouth.

'Ready now...?' he asked thickly, steel eyes mocking.

'I'll never be ready for you...!' she whispered, heart slamming like mad.

'No?' he drawled against her mouth. 'Not even if I stripped you naked, very slowly, and——'

'Oh!' Her face flamed with furious excitement. 'You really are an insolent bastard! How dare you say such things to me?'

'I'll have your clothes off for that, Miss Shaw!' he said softly, and then his hands slid up to cover her full breasts, and as she gasped hotly his fingers tugged down the black bodice fractionally to expose her bare breasts, sending shock waves of excitement through her.

'No!' She arched in appalled desire, her hands clutching his strong neck, and suddenly their mouths were almost touching, and as his grey gaze fell to her parted lips Caroline gave a hoarse moan of need, and a second later Mark's mouth was on hers, kissing her with a demanding passion that made her melt like molten fire.

He was pushing her back against the cushions, his mouth burning on hers, and she went helplessly, opening to him, her mouth as defenceless against him as her body. Dizzy, she moaned as she felt his strong hands close over her breasts, stroking the erect nipples and making her gasp over and over again, her heart thudding faster as he kissed her forcefully, and she knew her nipples were painfully erect and that her own foolish hands were stroking over Mark's neck, pushing restlessly into his thick black hair as she lost her mind to the power of her body.

The zip of her dress flared slowly down, and she started to moan in hoarse protest against his hard mouth, but he was ruthless, merciless, and he was already tugging down the black dress until she was bared to the waist.

'God, I've wanted to do this for so long...!' he bit out thickly, and his steel eyes flashed down over her body, and when he lifted his gaze back to her face he was breathing harshly.

'Don't look at me like that!' she heard her hoarse voice whisper.

He stared at her mouth, then made a harsh sound under his breath as his mouth claimed it, and the kiss became desperate, their mouths moving in abject hunger. He stroked her nipples, his fingers urgent, and her whole body reacted as though burned as she arched against him, mindless now, her whole world concentrated on his passionate mouth, his strong hands and that hard, commanding body which forced her to respond.

The harsh rap at the door made them both start, their heads jerking, eyes opening in dazed incomprehension, and the spell broke as effectively as if they had been given a douse of cold water.

Caroline stared at him in horror, and gave a hoarse cry, covering her bare breasts with her arms, hiding her face by turning away from him, eyes tightly closed.

'Who the hell is that?' Mark was breathing hoarsely, his face darkly flushed.

'Room service!' Caroline whispered in sick humiliation. 'I ordered coffee...!'

He was silent for a moment, his mouth tightening. Then he swore hoarsely under his breath, and sat up. She felt him staring at her as she flinched from him, covering herself with defenceless hands.

'Come here!' he said with an impatience in his voice, but his hands were surprisingly gentle as he pulled her into a sitting position, zipping up her dress with deft fingers.

'Answer it, Mark!' she said hoarsely, her face scarlet with self-contempt. 'He might use his key and——'

'And find me making love to my beautiful secretary?' he drawled mockingly, and bent his head to kiss her mouth, a faint smile in his grey eyes. 'My God, Caroline, you really are innocent, aren't you?'

She winced, sickened by her own behaviour, and feeling deeply ashamed as she watched him get to his feet and stride to the door.

Caroline sat immobile on the sofa, a prisoner of her own shame, and stared through her lashes as Mark admitted the waiter and told him coolly to put the tray of coffee on the coffee-table in front of her.

She had never before admitted the depths of her sexual desire for Mark Rider, but she was forced to now, she was absolutely staring into the mirror of truth and all she could see was herself lost in a whirlpool of excitement as she let him strip her practically naked...

'You're not going to have time to drink that coffee,' Mark said, walking back to her when the waiter had gone. 'It's almost seven-twenty. We're going to be late unless we leave immediately.'

'Yes, of course!' she whispered, standing up.

He moved in front of her, staring down into her white face. 'I wish to God we didn't have to go tonight!' he said broodingly, his hands moving to her long hair. 'What I want is to stay here and make love to you for the next week!'

Horrified, she stepped back from him, her eyes accusing. 'I'm going to marry Stephen Daly! Doesn't that mean anything to you?'

'Damn Stephen Daly!' he said bitingly. 'And damn marriage!'

'You can't just dismiss it like that!'

'Watch me,' he said through his teeth, and turned on his heel, striding to the door, scooping his black cashmere coat from the chair he had flung it on when he walked in. 'Get your coat. We don't have time to hang around here having tedious arguments about your bloody fiancé!'

Caroline sensed that violence in him as he waited for her by the door, his face hard and his eyes like steel.

Without another word, she followed him from the room, sliding into her coat as she walked. She was bitterly aware of the fact that her own attraction to him was now undeniable. For months she had been able to keep him at a distance from her. She had known from the beginning that he would be able to destroy all her defences with one kiss.

'We'll talk later tonight,' Mark said broodingly as they rode down in the lift together. 'I'll come to your room.' His narrowed eyes studied her bent head intently. 'Got that?'

She nodded, silent and filled with apprehension. She didn't want to look at him. As for him coming to her room—well, she'd argue that one out later. She wasn't letting him into her room ever again.

The lift doors slid open. They walked out into the foyer.

'I'll get the car,' Mark strode coolly beside her. 'You wait——' He broke off as they stepped out through the glass doors. 'My God. It's been snowing the whole time we've been here!'

Caroline stared at the white blanket covering the ground. 'Is it safe to drive?'

He frowned. 'It should be. But we'll have to go slowly.'

'At least the snow seems to have stopped. Maybe it will melt . . .'

'I hope so,' Mark said flatly, and strode to the car park. 'Wait there for me!' He flung that last command over his broad shoulder with his usual brand of hard authority.

Caroline shivered in her white coat, hands deep in pockets. The black Bentley purred towards her, exhaust fumes freezing as they entered the ice-cold air.

Rachey's house was something of a Georgian manor, set back from the road with private gates and a large parkland estate. The guard waved them through, and they sped up to the elegant front door.

A butler greeted them, led them through a wide white-painted hallway to a drawing-room where a fire crackled in an Adam grate and elegant furniture gleamed pale peach under a warm chandelier.

'Mark!' Jack Rachey was a tall, handsome man of thirty with dark hair and dark eyes. He had inherited the company from his father a year ago, and didn't have the same flair as his late father for marketing the product. 'Good to see you.'

'Hello, Jack,' Mark drawled coolly, shaking his hand. 'You look well.'

'Thanks! So do you!' Jack turned his dark eyes smilingly to Caroline. 'And Miss Shaw! It's a pleasure to see you again!'

'And you.' Caroline tensed, surprised when he embraced her, because they'd only met a handful of times, and always at business meetings. But she kissed his handsome cheek as though they were old friends, bearing in mind that Mark wanted her to be nice to Rachey. 'It's lovely to see the famous Rachey house at last! I've heard so much about it in the Press.'

'You must come and stay one day.' Jack looked debonair in a grey suit. 'I often have weekend parties. It's such a big house and there's only me and the staff. I love having house guests. Especially when they're as beautiful as you!'

'Oh!' Caroline felt rather sorry for him, all alone in this great big mansion miles from anywhere. 'That's very sweet of you! I'd love to.'

Mark gave her a deadly look with those steel eyes. Then he said tightly, 'I have the contract with me, Jack...'

They started to talk business, and Caroline frowned as she sat down on the couch, wondering why he had given her such an angry look.

'Gin and tonic, Miss Shaw?' Jack asked her from the drinks cabinet.

'Thank you.' She smiled. 'And do call me Caroline!'

Mark's eyes narrowed on her face, making her own eyes widen at the look he gave her. What on earth was the matter with him? He had specifically asked her to be nice to Jack Rachey!

They had a drink each, then went into the dining-room. It was an elegant showpiece of a room with mahogany table and portraits. Dinner was served by the housekeeper. It was beef consommé followed by sole in a delicious creamy white wine sauce.

'I just don't know who to trust,' Jack Rachey was saying after the main course, and after a great deal of chilled Chablis. 'I've only had the company for a year, of course, and I get advice from everyone.'

'Your decision to take marketing out of old hands was the right one,' Mark told him. 'My art staff are all under thirty-five and four of them are young women in their early twenties.'

'They're very modern and forward-looking,' Caroline affirmed.

'Like you?' Jack Rachey smiled at her, charm in his eyes.

Caroline laughed. 'No, I'm a secretary!'

'You're the sexiest little secretary I've ever seen!' Jack murmured, eyes drifting to her mouth. 'I don't suppose you'd come and work for me? That old dragon Father left me is driving me mad!'

'She gets the job done, though,' Mark said flatly, eyes narrowing. 'And you obviously don't!'

Jack gave a harsh sigh. 'You understand me, Mark! It's all true, I'm afraid. I'm just not cut out to be a big boss. I was much happier being an heir. That was fun. Driving about in sports cars, having parties, drinking champagne...'

Caroline smiled at him. 'Poor Jack...!' He really was a complete idiot, but at least he had a sense of humour.

Jack warmed to her even more, putting a hand on her wrist. 'I've got lots of photos stashed away of my wonderful ex-life. I don't suppose you'd care to see them?'

'That would be lovely,' Caroline said, smiling, and glanced at Mark, hoping he was pleased with the way she was being nice to him, and almost blanched at the steely look he gave her instead.

But Jack was standing, wine glass in one hand, Caroline's wrist in the other, and leading her out of the dining-room, talking closely to her as he held her hand. Mark followed them with a hard expression.

'Wait there,' Jack told Caroline, leading her to the sofa.

Mark stood in the centre of the room, his face a cold hard mask. 'It's late and we don't have time for a trip down memory lane.'

Caroline's eyes widened at his deliberate rudeness.

Jack straightened, walking round with a photo album. 'Just one album, old sport,' he drawled, and sank down beside her, very close beside her. 'Miss Caroline Shaw and I are getting on like a house on fire!'

Mark's teeth bared in a smile. 'Miss Shaw is an expert at setting houses on fire.'

'I noticed your ring earlier,' Jack said lazily, and picked up her left hand, studying the diamond. 'Rather a tiny stone. Not your usual style, surely, Mark?'

Mark studied him, his face a tough mask, and said nothing. He didn't need to. His eyes were dangerous enough.

'It's not Mark's ring,' Caroline said tensely. 'I'm engaged to someone else.'

'Ah... I thought it couldn't be Mark's,' Jack said softly.

Mark's eyes narrowed.

Jack Rachey smiled mischievously. 'Why *have* you never married, Mark? I would have thought *one* of your many women had the right ingredients! And you are such an eligible man, aren't you? Rich, powerful——'

'A fascinating discussion,' Mark drawled coolly. 'But it's started to snow again. I must insist we leave at once.'

Caroline quickly got to her feet. 'Thank you for a lovely evening, Jack,' she said.

'How long are you staying in the area?' Jack asked, standing too.

'Until Sunday,' Mark said flatly, hands thrust in black trouser pockets as he eyed Jack contemptuously.

'Really?' Jack looked pleased. 'In that case, you don't mind if I invite your beautiful secretary back for lunch tomorrow? So she can see my photos, of course.'

'Caroline is here to work,' Mark said. 'Not play.'

'Then in that case,' said Jack with a smooth smile, 'you must come too, Mark. You can work while we play. How's that?'

Mark's eyes were like steel knives. 'Fine. What time shall we get here?'

'Better make it one o'clock.' Jack smiled. 'I never get up until the crack of lunch. I like to eat at around two. Makes for a nice big afternoon breakfast.'

'One o'clock, then,' Mark said with a contemptuous flick of his lashes over the younger man. 'Caroline . . . ?'

CHAPTER FOUR

THEY drove home in a tense silence. When the Bentley pulled up outside the hotel, Mark got out without a word, his face hard. Caroline got out too, walked after him, and almost slipped in the snow.

Mark's strong hand was suddenly at her elbow as he supported her, treating her to a hard look through his carved lids.

He was so tough, yet underneath that steel exterior she glimpsed a deep tenderness. He seemed to fight that capacity for tenderness. It seemed to make him angry, as though he hated himself for such a weakness and wanted to drive it out of his personality.

In the lift, the tense silence persisted. Caroline couldn't stand it any more, so she said, 'Are you angry with me, Mark?'

'Yes, I damned well am.' He looked at her with narrowed eyes. 'And you know why! You spent the whole evening deliberately twisting that conceited bastard round your little finger!'

'I wasn't flirting with Jack Rachey!' Caroline cut in angrily. 'I was doing what you asked—being nice to him!'

'You were a damned sight friendlier with him,' he said through his teeth, 'than you ever have been with any other man I've seen you with!'

'Because you asked me to be!'

'I keep asking you to take your clothes off—it doesn't seem to have much effect!'

Her face flamed. 'You specifically said before we left London that you wanted me here because Jack had a soft spot for me!'

'And you really took advantage of it, didn't you?' he said tightly as the lift doors opened. Face hard, he strode out of the lift and Caroline followed him, her green eyes flaring.

'I did not take advantage of anything!' she said furiously, hurrying to keep up with his long-legged stride. 'Jack's obviously not interested in running that company! He just wants to drink champagne all day! When he asked me to look at his photos, what was I supposed to do? Tell him to grow up?'

He turned suddenly, grey eyes narrowing. 'Is that what you thought?'

Caroline almost bumped into him, breathless. 'Of course!'

'You didn't like him, then?'

'He was nice enough...' she said huskily. 'But silly, pampered and still a little boy beneath the debonair playboy façade.'

'And you don't like little boys?' he murmured, smiling sardonically.

'I don't find them attractive, if that's what you mean.'

A sardonic smile touched his mouth. The black lashes flickered on his razor-sharp cheekbones. There was a peculiar stillness about him for a second.

'Go and get ready for bed...' he murmured, and bent his head, brushing his mouth burningly against hers.

Then he turned and unlocked his door while she just stared at him. A second later his door had closed. Baffled, Caroline walked along the corridor to her room, next door, walking slowly in, throwing her key, coat and bag on to the chair.

Being here with Mark was a minefield of danger for her. He demanded everything he could get from her—including as much personal information as possible. She was deeply aware of him as it was. Having to share her thoughts and feelings with him was the very last thing she wanted.

Caroline went into the bathroom, showered quickly, then changed into her favourite nightgown. It was black lace, seductive and feminine. Her long silken hair fell in tousled brown-gold curls down her slender back.

Suddenly, her bedroom door opened.

Gasping, she turned, staring in breathless shock as Mark stepped in. Her heart was suddenly bolting at a gallop. She gripped the edge of the dressing-table behind her with shaking hands.

'How did you get in?' she asked in a constricted voice.

'There's a connecting door.' He walked towards her, his hard body predatory, the black dressing-gown he wore made of thick silk, exposing the tanned flesh of his chest, and the long muscular legs. 'They asked at the desk if we wanted the key when we first checked in.'

'I didn't hear them!' she accused hotly.

'You walked away,' he said, reaching her, towering over her. 'Hotel staff are very discreet. So are lovers staying in hotels in connecting rooms.'

'I didn't know they were connecting!' she said huskily, trembling with a desire so deep that it made her stomach ache with pain.

'No,' he said, staring at her mouth. 'But you did know I was coming here like this. Didn't you?'

Mute, she shook her head, bright hair spilling over bare shoulders, and Mark's steel eyes seemed to fragment as they slid slowly down her body, her skin glowing, blood pulsing through her veins and making her full breasts beat with visible movement beneath that seductive nightdress.

'I knew you'd be breathtaking at night!' he said tautly, raising his eyes to her flushed face. 'But even I couldn't have imagined this. You're superb...!'

'You have to get out of here...' she whispered threadily, unable to move, her own eyes moving in rapid urgency over his broad shoulders, the black hair revealed at his chest. 'This isn't right! You know it isn't!'

His hands curved slowly over her full breasts.

'Oh, God...!' she moaned, eyes closing, heart slamming crazily. 'Mark... I don't want this to happen! I've made that clear!'

'You do want it,' he said thickly, and slid his strong hands to her waist. 'You seduce me every time you look at me. Your body's alive with electricity whenever I'm near. It's the same for me, Caroline.' His eyes were fierce silver as he stared down at her provocative mouth. 'I can't stand it much longer!'

They were standing very close now. Her lips were parted and she was unable to move. The last eight months seemed to be rushing in on her, clamouring like a frantic prisoner beating on a locked door to be released.

'Tell me you can't stand it either!' he said thickly, his hands tightening on her waist. 'Tell me...!'

'No...' she said in a hoarse, shaking voice. 'I can't stand it any more than you can!'

Mark's face filled with dark colour as he pulled her into his arms and his hard mouth closed over hers.

They kissed desperately. Caroline's hands were in his hair, his mouth was burning like fire over hers and she was open to him, past denial and rejection, kissing him back with equal hunger as he pressed her slender, sensual body against his and she moaned with excitement.

'I don't know how we've worked together for so long!' Mark said shakingly, his mouth trailing over her white throat. 'Oh, God, I want you so much!'

'Mark . . . !' she said in hoarse weakness, and he made a rough sound under his breath, picked her up in his arms as though she were a gazelle, and carried her to the bed.

She was flung down on it, breathless, staring up at him with hot molten green eyes as he joined her, his face a hard mask of desire, steel eyes shooting hot silver fire at her.

'You've been driving me insane!' he said thickly as his hard body covered hers, and his hands shook on her soft, bare shoulders. 'Eight months of wanting this . . . I can't believe I'm lying on a bed with you!'

'I was fighting it!' she confessed hoarsely. 'I fought so hard, Mark, so very hard . . .'

'And now you can't fight any longer!' he said thickly, and then his mouth was burning on hers, and her lips were opening as he arched above her in dominant passion, his strong hands moving with urgency over her body, tightening on her narrow waist, sliding up her ribcage, feeling the fierce thud of her heart like a captive bird before those strong hands slid up to cup her full, swelling breasts.

He raised his head, breathing thickly, and his eyes flashed to her breasts as his fingers tugged down the lacy

bodice of her nightdress and his breathing thickened
further.

'You're so beautiful!' he whispered, and one hand slid
over her bare breast as she lay beneath him, shivering
with fevered desire. 'And so damned sexy...' His mouth
closed sensually over hers again, his strong hands tugging
her nightdress to her hips. 'Let me see you...let me...'

'I won't let you make love to me!' she warned in a
voice that shook with desire. 'You know it's impossible,
Mark!' Her hands stopped him removing the nightdress
and her body throbbed with the knowledge of her nudity
beneath it.

'Why?' he asked thickly. 'Because you're engaged to
that blond boy? You don't feel like this for him,
Caroline! I saw you dance with him and I saw you look
at him.' A hard smile curved his mouth. 'You don't smile
at him the way you do at me.'

'How do I smile at you, Mark...?' she whispered
softly, stroking his strong neck with seductive fingers.

'Oh, God,' he said thickly, eyes darkening, 'you little
seductress!' and then his mouth was closing over hers
with sensual hunger, his hands moving swiftly to cover
her breasts, stroke the erect nipples, making her shoot
into hot delirium, her breath coming faster as her fingers
moved rythmically over his neck, stroking down to his
powerful chest.

Shaking, she was drowning in pleasure as their mouths
clung lingeringly. Her hands slid his black silk robe a
little apart because she wanted to touch him so badly,
and she felt the thudding of his heart against her shaking
hands, felt the crackle of black hairs against her flesh.

His hard body moved against her with slow, rhythmic
skill. She was sliding against him, eyes closed, mouth

clinging to his. His hands moved over her bare breasts, fondling them as she gasped in dazed excitement against his commanding mouth.

When she felt his strong hands move to her slim thighs, start to push the silky nightdress up, she panicked, fighting him suddenly, tearing her mouth from his.

'No!' Her voice was shaky with arousal. 'For God's sake, Mark!'

'I've thought of nothing else for months!' he said against her mouth. 'And nor have you!'

Her eyes closed in appalled acknowledgement.

'You knew I'd come for you tonight!' he whispered against her throat. 'And you tormented me at Rachey's! Didn't you? It was deliberate! You flirted with that swine all night, and you watched me as you did it, enjoying my rage!'

'You asked me to be nice to him!' she said against his mouth.

'Yes,' he said tightly, 'and you took it to the absolute limit! I had to sit and watch you giving him those seductive looks from under your lashes, laughing at everything he said! I wanted to kill you!'

She lowered her lashes, murmuring softly, 'You almost sound jealous...'

He tensed, eyes narrowing and his face was very hard as he drawled, 'I can assure you I'm not. I just don't like seeing my secretary throw herself at my clients. It's hardly acceptable conduct, is it?'

Her eyes flashed up in ill-concealed fury. 'I did not throw myself at him! Why should I? I'm an engaged woman! Soon I'll be a married woman! I've never had a casual affair in my life!' Her eyes flashed over him with anger and a desire to hurt. 'How many lovers have you had, Mark? Or don't you even remember!'

He studied her in tense silence, and she saw a flash of violence in his grey eyes. 'My past is irrelevant. It's the present I'm interested in.'

'And I want the future!' she said thickly.

'The plastics man? Don't be absurd, Caroline! You're not in love with him. He doesn't make you lose your head when he kisses you. Far from it. You can hold him off till doomsday like a little pet dog.' His eyes darkened as he said huskily, 'But you can't hold me off. Not for longer than three seconds maximum before you surrender...'

'Surrender isn't on my list of future achievements,' she said tightly, her hands on his broad shoulders. 'Only marriage is on that list, and I intend to get it, Mark.'

His mouth hardened. Suddenly, his hands were untying the belt of his dressing-gown.

'You can't!' she broke out hoarsely, stopping him with shaking hands. 'I won't let you do it!'

'You want me!' he said thickly, his mouth closing over hers, bringing a rush of sweet pleasure and excitement to her body as he renewed his lovemaking with exquisite skill, and she knew she was going to have to fight.

'No!' she cried, and started to struggle again, her eyes bitter as she fought him, slapping his face blindly as she tried to get away, panic making her arms flail like windmills, dimly aware of his harsh cry of anger as he took her wrists in a biting grip and pinned them to the bed, arching over her.

'All right!' he said furiously, eyes blazing. 'I won't take you just yet! Calm down, for God's sake, Caroline! We can talk about this for a moment! There's no need to lose your head!' He drew a ragged breath, staring down at her panic-stricken face.

Hot tears stung her eyes and she lay there in bitter silence for a long moment, breathing hard, her mouth shaking as she realised how close she was to letting him take her.

'I'll release you in a second,' he said under his breath, watching her intently. 'I don't want you to turn into a whirlwind, though. Just lie opposite me and face me. We'll talk. I have a proposition.'

Trembling, she nodded her head, and he slowly released her, moving away from her, lying on his side, one strong hand possessive on her waist as she turned towards him, naked to the waist, and felt his grey eyes move restlessly over her body as her heartbeat shook in her flat stomach.

Caroline swallowed, said huskily, 'Mark, I know it must seem as though I'm prepared to have an affair with you. But I'm not. I don't want to feel this way! I don't like it! It's too strong, too——'

'But you do feel it,' he said thickly. 'And now that I've brought it to a head you've admitted it.'

She lowered her lashes, face flooding with colour.

He watched her in brooding silence. 'We both feel the same. I think we may as well accept that this attraction isn't going to go away after just one night. Therefore—the sensible course of action is to set you up in a flat.'

Her eyes opened. 'What . . . ?'

'I want you to become my mistress.' Mark said under his breath, 'I'm a rich man, Caroline. I'll be more than generous. You can have a flat on Park Lane, a sports car and a big allowance.'

The insulting offer took her breath away, made it impossible to speak for a moment, and she just lay there staring at him, feeling the drum of hatred in her veins as it grew.

'Well?' he asked under his breath, touching her face with one strong hand. 'What do you say?'

She gave an angry smile, hating him. 'I'm so flattered, Mark! I can hardly believe my luck! It's every young girl's dream!' Her voice rose with bitterness, green eyes filling with hot tears. 'My God, you really know how to insult me, don't you? And you wonder why I've kept you at arm's length! You wonder why I wouldn't let you within a fifty-mile radius of me!' She was shaking as she finished, her voice hoarse.

'You wouldn't let me near you because you knew this would happen!' he said tensely, eyes narrowing. 'You knew you'd lose your head and respond to me, Caroline. Don't start lying about that again, or we'll be back to square one!'

'All right!' she said fiercely. 'I'm attracted to you! So what? That doesn't mean I have to act on it!'

'You already have!' he said, touching her face.

'Then it stops here!' She trembled, her face burning. 'I'd rather die than even consider accepting your insulting offer!'

'What did you expect?' he demanded harshly. 'Marriage?'

She looked quickly away, face flaming.

He gave an incredulous laugh, staring. 'My God! You did, didn't you? You thought I'd marry you!'

'Shut up!' she said hotly, flashing angry green eyes back to his face. 'And get out of my room! I'd rather die than let a man like you make love to me. Love! My

God—you wouldn't even be doing that, would you? You'd be using me, the way you've used all your women—as though I was a business partner, not a woman with thoughts and feelings!'

There was a taut silence. The tone of her voice made it very clear that she meant what she said, her dislike and anger blazing from her eyes. Mark watched her without speaking for a long moment. She could sense the anger in him. He was bristling with it.

'Do I take it that your answer to my proposition is no?' he enquired tightly, arching black brows.

'Of course it's no!' she said bitterly. 'Did you really think I'd allow you to treat me like that? To set me up like a courtesan, pay me money and shower me with expensive luxuries while you come and go like my favourite client?' Her mouth shook as she stared at him contemptuously. 'You must have been out of your mind!'

'I must be!' he agreed tightly, suddenly pushing her on to her back, his eyes like hot silver as he arched over her. 'To let you talk me down! I could have had you just now and we both know it!'

Her eyes challenged him. 'You think so, Mark?'

'I know it!' he said under his breath. 'And now I'm tired of your little games! I think it's time I just damned well took what we both want—don't you?'

His mouth closed over hers in a burning kiss, making her catch her breath with intolerable desire, hating herself for wanting him, hating herself for this dark excitement, for loving the feel of his hard hands on her bare breasts, stroking her nipples while she struggled not to show how much she wanted him.

If she responded—even once—he would push her over the brink and take her. She knew it. He knew it. Something in his dark heart drove him to do it.

Caroline lay still beneath him, her mouth indifferent, her body utterly unmoving. Mark sensed her withdrawal, and his kisses became harder, his hands more urgent as they moved over her body.

Mark raised his head, breathing harshly. 'What the hell are you playing at?' His eyes flared with anger. 'You're doing this deliberately! You want me! I can feel your heart beating like a damned drum!' His hands tightened angrily on her shoulders. 'You're just pretending not to respond!'

'Am I, Mark?' she asked, fighting to retain her willpower to resist.

'Yes!' he bit out thickly. 'Stop it and kiss me back!' His mouth closed fiercely over hers, hurting her now with ruthless determination to reach inside her, make her respond.

Caroline lay still and unmoving.

'Stop this!' he said shakingly, raising his head. 'Stop it!'

'You're stronger than me,' she said tightly. 'No one will come and help me if you just take me. That's what you said you were going to do, isn't it? Just take what you wanted! Well, go ahead, Mark. I'm sure you'll enjoy it. After all—you don't care about my feelings, do you? All you want is your own pleasure.'

He stared at her in furious silence, his face dark red and his eyes breaking into little silver daggers as he saw the fierce determination in her face.

Suddenly, he was pushing her away from him, getting off the bed, tightening the belt of his silk robe, the air vibrating with tension as he raked a hand through his black hair, looking down at her.

'Given up, Mark?' Caroline asked, her voice shaking.

'Damn right!' he bit out thickly, his eyes bitter as they flared over her. 'I wouldn't touch you again if you went down on your knees and begged me to!' He strode out of the room, slamming the door behind him.

Why should I feel so bad? she thought furiously. He had no right to do that, to come to my bedroom and throw me on the bed, demand that I make love with him.

Her face flushed with angry colour. It was true that they were mutually attracted—but it was just a sexual attraction. There was nothing else to it, and she would be damned if she'd give in to that and ruin herself in her own eyes and his.

As for asking her to be his mistress . . . she was almost apoplectic with rage. Didn't he realise how insulting that was? She would feel cheap even considering it. She felt cheap enough being asked point-blank to do it. How would she feel if she actually became his mistress?

The question was—could she fight him?

Well, she thought determinedly, I fought him off just now. Surely I can do it again? Surely I'm strong enough to resist that intolerable temptation he offers . . .

CHAPTER FIVE

NEXT morning, Caroline was woken by an angry knock on her bedroom door. Blinking sleep out of her eyes, she stared, disorientated, at the door and the room around her. Memory flooded back to her.

The angry knock on her door came again. Caroline sat up, dragging the coverlet over her black lace nightgown to cover her breasts, her long hair sleep-tousled, her face softened by sleep.

'Who is it?' she called in obvious pretence.

'Who do you think?' Mark's voice said flatly.

Her pulses leapt, but she kept her voice cool. 'Come in.'

The door opened. He was hard-faced, wearing black trousers and a black V-neck cashmere sweater. He looked intolerably sexy, his powerful chest outlined by that black sweater, and he looked more dangerous than ever, his steel eyes knifing through her.

'It's almost ten.' His voice was hostile. 'I thought I'd better wake you.'

'Thank you.' Caroline said huskily, lowering her lashes.

His mouth tightened. 'There's no need to look away like that!'

She flushed, plucking at the coverlet.

'I'm not going to force an argument about last night!' Mark said flatly. 'I suggest we just forget it happened!'

'OK,' she said huskily, nodding, her face averted and vulnerable, and she knew as well as he did that sweeping it under the carpet was not going to work for either of them.

His eyes narrowed. 'Well, look at me, damn you!'

Slowly, she raised her green eyes.

There was a fraught silence.

'I've had breakfast,' Mark said tightly. 'Do you want anything?'

'I'd like some coffee, please,' she said huskily, then, 'We have to leave at around half-twelve, don't we?'

'Yes. And before we go, we have to discuss an effective strategy for getting Jack Rachey's signature on the contract.'

'Very wise,' she said, studying his hard mouth through her lashes.

His eyes narrowed. 'After last night's performance from him, I think he's just enjoying the game.'

Caroline nodded her agreement.

'I could say the same about you,' Mark bit out suddenly under his breath.

'Don't,' she said huskily, pulses leaping with response.

'Is that what it is?' He took a step forward, bristling with aggression, eyes probing her face. 'A game? If it is, Caroline, I——'

'I thought we weren't going to talk about last night?' she said on a note of husky alarm.

His mouth tightened. 'Fine. We won't. Just get up and get dressed!' He turned on his heel, walked out of the door and slammed it behind him.

She flinched at the slam of that door, then made a wry face. The build-up over these eight months had reached explosion-point. She took a shower, blow-dried her hair, applied make-up and got dressed, choosing a stark navy blue shift dress with a white lace collar.

When she had zipped it up, she studied it in the mirror. It was short and severe, but very sexy, especially with her hair falling softly over one eye and her long legs lengthened by high black heels. But it was the most professional and starkly tailored dress she had with her, so it would just have to do.

Mark stared with brooding hostility when she walked into the living-room, his eyes moving restlessly over her, then away. He was on the sofa, strong arms spread out either side, his powerful chest on display.

Caroline sat in an armchair a few feet from him.

'Come and sit here,' Mark said, eyes narrowed, and patted the space on the sofa beside him.

Her eyes met his warily. 'I don't think that's a good idea . . .'

'Do as you're told,' he said with an edge to his voice.

She got up and walked to him, sinking down next to him, watching him through her lashes as she felt the powerful awareness intensify now they were so close.

Mark watched her with narrowed eyes, then said curtly, 'Pour the coffee?'

'Yes, sir!' she said tightly.

He laughed, drawling sneeringly, 'Well, you're the one who's going to be the little *hausfrau*, aren't you? It'll be good practice for you.'

Caroline's mouth tightened with fury, but she didn't want another argument with him. She could guess how it would end: in a violently passionate kiss.

Drawing an unsteady breath, she leaned forward and poured the coffee, aware of his mocking, sadistic smile as he watched her. Suddenly, he opened his briefcase and took out a sheaf of papers, once more the cool professional with a sharp eye for advertising.

They worked steadily. Mark ordered more coffee at eleven-thirty. Caroline leafed through the story-boards, graphic designs and the contract, and they discussed the account in an air of tension.

'We're going to have to leave,' Mark said at twenty-five past twelve, and put the documents back in the briefcase, snapping the lid shut. 'You can take this. He'll want to spend most of the time talking to you.'

Caroline nodded. 'I'll try to keep the conversation on business. After all—that is the purpose of this weekend.'

There was a little silence as they suddenly looked at each other, and the flash of desire in his eyes made that excitement sweep through her veins again as she looked at him warily through her lashes. Her heart was thumping. She felt her gaze move inexorably to his firm, sensual mouth. She wanted him to kiss her...quickly, she looked away, swallowing hard.

Mark said under his breath, 'Get your coat!'

Caroline got up without a word and walked to her bedroom, getting her coat and sliding into it, her hands shaking. This was going to drive her mad. The sooner this minefield of a weekend was over, the better.

They went down to the foyer in the lift.

'Snowing again,' Mark said flatly as they stood inside the foyer doors and stared out. 'We really picked the wrong weekend.'

'Maybe we shouldn't go,' Caroline said, frowning. 'That's almost a blizzard, and the roads will be treacherous.'

He shot her a steely look. 'I'm not going through this weekend again!' He pushed open the door. 'I'll get the car! You wait here!'

Caroline watched him stride off, his black coat blowing in the icy wind as snow engulfed him, blurring him from her view as the snowflakes swirled like a thick white mist.

Minutes later, the car was inching slowly towards her, its headlights flaring.

Caroline slid in beside him, shivering, and the interior of the Bentley was below zero, making her breath freeze in front of her as she huddled into her coat.

'The heater won't take long to warm up,' Mark said flatly, pulling away with a smooth flare of power, eyes narrowed on the hazardous road.

Caroline peered through the snow. 'It looks dangerous to me. I don't think we should go.'

'Are you prepared to stay here for another four or five days with me, Caroline?' he drawled mockingly.

She was silent, staring at his hard profile.

'I know I said I wouldn't go near you again,' he said cynically, 'but a week alone in a hotel with you would leave me with no alternative. And you wouldn't want that—would you?'

Caroline lowered her lashes.

'Would you?' he taunted, anger lacing his hard voice.

She looked up angrily. 'No!'

He gave a harsh laugh, then drawled cynically, 'No, of course not. God forbid that you should want me to take you to bed.'

'I don't want you to,' she said tightly.

'You want me as much as I want you!' he said under his breath, and she had to look away, unable to reply, afraid to argue with him in case he stopped the car and proved it to her. One kiss...that was all it would take...just one kiss and she knew she would be unable to resist, knew she would find herself kissing him back, pushing her hands through his hair, curving her body against him with wanton abandon.

I mustn't let it happen, she thought in despair. I must keep him at arm's length for the rest of this stupid weekend.

They were crawling along the main road towards Rachey's, and visibility was poor. They passed the occasional car, also crawling along with headlights on. The snow was whirling like a thousand tiny white dervishes.

'If you weren't already engaged to Daly,' Mark asked coolly, 'would your answer have been different last night?'

'No,' she said under her breath. 'I still wouldn't have let you make love to me.'

He gave a cynical smile. 'I meant your answer, Caroline, to my proposition.'

She looked at him angrily, green eyes hating him. 'Your insulting little offer last night was hardly every young girl's dream.'

'I don't deal in dreams,' he said flatly. 'I deal in hard facts.'

'What's so factual about offering to make me your mistress?'

His brows arched. 'It suits my needs. I want to make love to you, I want to know you're not making love to anyone else, and I want you on call twenty-four hours a day.'

'My God!' she spat, almost incoherent with fury. 'Will you listen to yourself? Do you have any idea how insulting you are? No, of course you don't! You just say what you want and expect to get it. I'll bet you didn't even think about what you were really offering me!'

A muscle jerked in his cheek as he turned off the main road slowly, driving along the first of the rabbit warren of little country lanes that led to Rachey's house.

'I did think about it,' he said tightly. 'In fact I've been thinking about it for months, Caroline.'

Her lashes flickered in surprise.

'Don't look so pleased about it!' he drawled, shooting her a steel look. 'Why do you think I threatened you with the sack if you didn't come away this weekend? I'd got to the point where I was ready to offer you the moon on a platter the minute I got you alone!'

She laughed angrily. 'Asking me to be your paid mistress is hardly the moon on a platter, Mark.'

'Well, I'm not going to offer marriage!' he said bitingly and his hands tightened on the wheel.

'Nobody asked you to!' she said defensively.

'Not much!' he said, his voice like a razor. 'I know exactly what you're holding out for, and you can forget it. Marriage! Don't make me laugh! I'm not the marrying kind and I certainly won't be forced to the altar by a green-eyed seductress like you!'

Caroline hated him bitterly, watching him as he drove along the narrow lanes, skilfully guiding the Bentley through the blizzard, across snowbound roads. She needed time to control herself, anger racing through her veins, and she breathed thickly, staring out of the window for a few tense minutes.

Then she turned and looked at him and asked tightly, 'Are we nearly there?'

A hard smile tightened his mouth. 'Dying to get away from my intolerable company, Miss Shaw?'

'What do you expect?' she said thickly. 'It was bad enough at the office, but I can barely think straight now!'

'That's because you want me to take you to bed!' he said tautly. 'Why the hell won't you just admit it, let me do it, and end this stalemate?'

'Why don't you end it?' she said fiercely.

'By marrying you!' He laughed, eyes intent on the blizzard as he drove. 'Go to hell! I wouldn't marry you if you——' A snowdrift suddenly loomed ahead of them. Mark veered the car away from it. They went into a skid. 'God!' he bit out, grappling with the wheel as it was wrenched from him, and Caroline sat in appalled silence as they spun and slithered crazily across the road, bumping up across the field as snow and grass flew at them and a second later they crashed into a brick wall.

Splintering chrome and steel and glass went on forever in slow motion as they were both flung forwards with the impact, the seatbelt digging into Caroline's windpipe and making her give a hoarse gasp at the same moment as she heard Mark's thick grunt of pain as he was rammed into the steering-wheel.

Then they were both jerked back against their seats, and there was a peculiar silence, the wind and snow blowing icily all around them as they sat staring at the brick wall and the mangled wreck of the bonnet.

'Are you all right?' Mark's harsh voice shook as he leaned towards her, a strong hand touching her cheek, turning her to face him. 'Caroline!'

'Yes...' She looked up, dazed and shocked. 'And you? I heard you cry out in pain as we hit——'

'It's nothing,' he said tersely. 'But this isn't. Look at my car!' His mouth hardened. 'Look at this blizzard. We'll be in trouble if we can't get the car to start.' He turned the ignition keys, but the engine didn't even respond.

Caroline watched him in growing panic.

'It's dead,' he said grimly. 'Presumably there are bits of engine lying on the ground at this very moment.' He unclipped his seatbelt suddenly. 'Come on. We can't stay here or we'll die.'

She quickly unclipped her own seatbelt. 'But where are we going to go?'

'That looks like a farmhouse beyond the wall,' he said flatly. 'I can't see any telephone wires, but at least it's shelter, and maybe the farmer will have a tractor or a Range Rover that can cope with this kind of weather.'

She shivered, staring at the blurred snowy outline of a small grey stone building beyond the wall. 'It's very small, whatever it is. It doesn't look like a farm to me.'

'Well, let's find out,' he said, and opened his car door.

The blast of icy wind and snow made her shiver, but she braved it herself, getting out of the car, head bent against that powerful wind as snow flew blindingly into her eyes.

Mark's strong hand groped for hers as he came round to her, and pulled her along with him. 'Just keep your head down!' he shouted at her above the sound of the wind. 'I'll lead the way!'

Stumbling in her high heels, she sank into snow four inches deep and it froze her ankle-bones, made them feel burnt with the cold, her face white and her long hair getting very damp.

'There are steps!' Mark shouted as they approached the small grey slate cottage.

Her eyes winced as snow flew into them, but she could see the steps vaguely, and Mark's strong hand in hers helped her up them. She was shivering violently, and her teeth were chattering with the cold as she stood beside him in front of the door.

He banged on it repeatedly, hunted for a doorbell, and time dragged on and on as no reply came.

'Nobody's home!' Mark shouted loudly above the howling blizzard. 'The place is deserted!'

'But there's nothing else for miles!' She felt panic set in. 'I can't even remember the last building we passed!'

His mouth tightened, black hair blowing wildly around his hard face. 'We'll have to break in!'

'We can't do that!' she said. 'It's not our house!'

'We'll die if we stay out here!'

'We could walk back to the main road!'

'We'd never reach it, Caroline!'

Her heart stopped beating as their eyes met and death flashed between them, drawing them suddenly into another world as they stood there and stared at each other while the wind howled and tore at them.

'I'll break a window!' Mark turned, strode against the wind to the front-room window a short distance away. His fist raised, drew back, then punched a hole through the glass.

'Mark, for God's sake…!' Caroline ran to him, seeing the blood spurt from his knuckles as the sound of broken glass was just audible above the storm. 'Look at your hand!'

He brushed her impatiently aside. 'I'm going to climb in. I'll open the front door for you. Wait here!' He

opened the window from inside, then climbed on to the
ledge and leapt in.

Caroline went back to the front door, snow stinging
her cheeks painfully. She was almost blue with cold, and
her feet were so numb that she thought her toes might
have broken off.

The sound of a heavy bolt drawing back came from
inside, then the door opened, and Mark was there,
hauling her inside with a strong, bloodied hand and
slamming the door after her.

'We're in luck! There's a fireplace in the living-room,'
Mark told her as he re-bolted the door against the storm.
'I'll have to repair that broken window somehow, but
that shouldn't be too hard.'

'Let me look at that hand.' Caroline shook snow from
her coat, fingers freezing as she stamped her snow-
covered feet, sending white ice in all directions to melt
on the dark green carpet. 'You're bleeding——'

'Don't fuss over me,' Mark bit out harshly, turning
and striding away from her.

She followed him into the living-room. An icy wind
blew in through the broken window.

'We'll have to block that hole up.' Mark frowned,
looking around.

'What about that fireguard?' she said, spotting a large
rectangular metal fireguard.

'Perfect,' said Mark, and strode to get it, picking it
up and lodging it firmly against the window, sealing it
effectively. 'Now, I'm going to explore the grounds, see
if there's a car or tractor or anything at all.'

'Mark,' she said flatly, 'you are dripping blood on to
the carpet. Will you please let me attend to that hand?'

He looked down at once, saw the drops of blood running from his hand to the floor and there was a little silence. Then he looked up and met her eyes.

Caroline said, 'There must be some kind of first-aid kit somewhere.'

His mouth tightened, but he gave a hard nod, and said, 'OK. But make it snappy. We don't have too much time if we're going to get out of here before the snow is eight inches deep.'

Caroline turned and went into the hall, her sense of direction leading her to a small kitchen, icy cold but quite spacious, with a table and four chairs around it.

It was dingy, so she flicked on the light but nothing happened.

'The light doesn't work,' she said, frowning.

Mark stepped back and tried the hall light. 'Neither does this one. It must be a power cut.'

'Oh, no...!' Caroline sighed. 'That's all we need!'

'You've obviously never lived in the country,' Mark drawled wryly.

'On the contrary,' she said, arching her brows, 'I lived in the country until I was twenty-one.'

He looked surprised, eyes moving over her. Then he said flatly, 'I think we're in luck again. That stove is gas-fired. If it works, we can keep warm, make some coffee before we leave.'

'Depending on whether or not you find a vehicle of some sort,' she said, and walked to the stove, switched on a gas jet. 'Thank God for that! It works.'

'I'll stick the kettle on,' he said, walking across the room.

Caroline started to look in cupboards. 'I'd better find some disinfectant for your hand.'

He filled the kettle, found a box of matches beside the gas stove, and lit a jet, putting a kettle on it. Caroline found a first-aid tin and walked over to him with it.

Mark watched her with narrowed eyes as she rummaged around in the tin, producing antiseptic cream and a clean bandage sealed in cellophane.

'Put your fingers under the tap.'

With an impatient sigh, he turned and held his hand under running water. When the blood was washed away, she inspected his hand, wincing at the cuts across his knuckles. Caroline cleansed the wounds with antiseptic cream and felt him tense.

'Does that sting?' she asked.

'No,' he said flatly, eyes narrowing. 'Now you can stop fussing. I don't want a dressing on it. I want to find a vehicle and get the hell out of here!' He turned on his heel, and strode out of the kitchen, slamming the door behind him.

CHAPTER SIX

CAROLINE took the kettle off the boil. If Mark meant what he said, he wouldn't want to hang around for coffee. Bleakly, she explored the downstairs of the house. He had been right about there being no telephone wires and no telephone. There was no way for them to call for help. The living-rooms were similar, but only one had a fireplace, and that was the one Mark had broken into. She wondered where the occupants were, and if they too were marooned somewhere in the snow. The fireplace yielded a scuttle full of coal, a pile of logs beside it, and some firelighters and matches. In the carved wood drinks cabinet she found a plentiful supply of liquor and soft drinks. There were books on the shelves, and two large comfortable sofas. She found some candles and lit four in the living-room, then went into the kitchen and lit another four.

Suddenly, a loud hammering on the front door made her run out into the hall and open it. The blizzard blew Mark inside, covered in snow and shivering, his face pinched with cold.

'Nothing!' he said tersely, striding past her, shaking snow from himself as he went. 'Not a damned thing!'

'Oh, no!' Caroline followed him. 'What are we going to do?'

'Make the best of it,' he said, pushing open the living-room door. 'Get that fire going, for a start. We might as well face it, Caroline.' He turned at the fireplace,

79

studying her with hard grey eyes. 'We could be stuck here until the morning.'

She swallowed, her heart missing a beat. 'All night...?'

'That blizzard means business.' He looked away, mouth tight. 'I could barely see in it. And the snow is at least four inches deep.'

'It's got to stop some time!' she said, appalled.

'And if it doesn't?' His dark brows arched. 'We might find ourselves snowed in for days, Caroline.'

Suddenly their eyes met and held in appalled silence.

Her heart missed a beat. 'What are we going to do?' she asked unsteadily, looking up, her chestnut-gold hair spilling damply around her beautiful face, green eyes glittering through long lashes.

Mark gave a hard grimace. 'I'll build the fire. You go in the kitchen and have a look around for food.'

Leaving the room, Caroline went into the kitchen with a sense of dread. How on earth would they get through the night? She put the kettle on again and lit one of the gas hobs, then lit them all in order to keep warmer.

There was a surprising amount of food. Rows of tins containing plenty of interesting dishes that would last them quite a long time if they were careful.

When she took Mark his coffee, she found him sitting in an armchair with a brooding expression on his face. He had pulled the chair close to the fire, which was now crackling as the logs caught light.

'There's quite a lot of food,' she told him. 'Do you want to hear the menu?'

A grudging smile touched his mouth. 'Well?'

'Spaghetti bolognese,' she said with an attempt at friendliness, 'or steak and kidney pie with new potatoes and peas. Or chicken and mushroom pie-filling with sweetcorn.' Her green eyes watched his face. 'Anything you fancy? Or shall I go on?'

'I'd prefer the spaghetti,' he said, and prodded the fire with a long steel poker, making logs spit and flames dance. 'I wonder where the occupants are? I'll have to reimburse them for that window, and everything else we might use.'

'I'll contribute half,' she said at once.

He gave her a hard, arrogant look. 'I think not.'

'I'm here too,' she said defensively. 'I'm using their——'

'And I've got ten times more money than you have,' he drawled, 'if not ten million times. Now, just leave it. I'll pay for everything.'

'I noticed dust on that pendulum,' she told him, gesturing to the grandfather clock in the corner. 'Nobody can have been here for at least a week. Maybe it's a holiday cottage.'

His brows drew in a frown. 'I hadn't thought of that.'

'If it is a holiday cottage, they won't be likely to come home equipped with a snow-plough and rescue us.'

Mark gave a brief laugh, sipping his black coffee. 'Quite!'

'Jack Rachey might, though,' she said, watching him carefully. 'He might already be on the phone to the hotel...'

'Don't make me laugh!' he drawled derisively. 'I should think he'll just shrug his shoulders when we don't turn up.'

'But it was a business appointment.' She frowned.

'He's not going to come and get us out of this, Caroline!' Mark said coolly. 'We're stuck with each other. Just accept it!'

'I'll go and cook lunch,' she said huskily, and left the room.

The kitchen was very warm now, the gas jets all on full blast, and so she took her coat off. She found an apron hanging on the back of the door, slipping it over her dress and tying it at the back.

Moving around efficiently, she prepared the spaghetti and opened the tin of bolognese sauce. She found a tin of devilled kidneys and put them into the sauce along with plenty of herbs and spices from the rack.

Half an hour later, she put her head round the kitchen door and called, 'Lunch!'

Mark came into the kitchen, intolerably sexy in the black cashmere sweater and black trousers, his hair dry now from the warmth of the fire, and his strong throat and chest gleaming with his tan.

'That smells delicious!' he admitted grudgingly.

Caroline turned. 'Just take a seat. I've laid the table.'

He studied the pine table with its knives and forks and place mats. 'A shame we haven't any wine.'

'There's a drinks cabinet in the living-room,' she said, serving spaghetti on to the two plates by the stove. 'I'm sure I saw some in there.'

'Really?' His eyes lit up, and he went off into the living-room, returning a moment later with a bottle of Chianti. 'Imagine keeping wine in the drinks cabinet! Most unorthodox!'

Caroline laughed, serving the spaghetti sauce on to the thick strands of pasta. Mark hunted for a bottle opener, then got two glasses and started opening the wine. They ate at the table, although they had to attack the parmesan cheese with a knife to hack it out of its solidified state.

'I feel almost human again,' Mark commented, leaning back in his chair, pushing his plate away and cradling his glass of red wine in one strong hand. 'It's amazing what a little food and warmth will do.'

She nodded, smiling benignly. 'They're innate needs.'

'Yes, of course,' he said, sipping his wine. 'What are the others? Food, shelter, comfort and security. There are four, aren't there.'

'We've got them all in this little cottage.' Caroline sipped her wine.

'Not quite all,' Mark said with a barbed smile.

Her green eyes flashed warily to his.

'Comfort is just another word for physical affection,' he said tightly, mouth hard. 'And there's precious little of that in here!'

Pulses leaping, she said huskily, 'I'll clear the dishes...'

'Very domesticated!' he drawled with a nasty smile. 'You really can't wait to get married, can you?'

Her mouth compressed. Glaring at him, she picked up the plates and walked to the sink.

'If only Stephen could see you now!' he mocked, watching her. 'The little *hausfrau* in her pinny!'

'You don't seriously think I *want* to do the washing up, do you?' she demanded, sliding the dishes into the water and adding washing-up liquid.

'No,' he said tightly. 'But you do want to get married.'

'What's wrong with that?' she said, washing a plate. 'Every woman wants to get married.'

'My mother didn't,' he said thickly.

The air between them suddenly crackled with violence. Slowly, she turned and stared at him.

He was white, his skin stretched tautly over his hard bones as he met her gaze and she saw violence flash out of his steel eyes, his mask suddenly ripped away.

That's it, she thought...

'I don't know why I said that.' His voice was thickly slurred. 'Forget I mentioned it.' There was a pause, then he stood up, saying abruptly, 'I'd better go and check on the fire.'

As the door closed, she was staring after him. Questions were buzzing around in her head. She forced herself to keep busy, cleaning the kitchen, her mind revolving around Mark, his complex, knife-edge personality and that hard-driving refusal to be human.

Suddenly, she noticed darkness falling outside, the snow still whirling violently. She had to go in there and face him at some point. Drawing an unsteady breath, she smoothed down her dress with damp palms, and walked out into the cold hall, then pushed open the living-room door.

Mark was lying on a sofa, on his side, reading a book.

He tensed as she came in, and so did she, the tension gripping her stomach like an iron fist.

His eyes were hostile as he said tightly, 'Hi!'

'My watch has stopped,' she said, watching him through her lashes. 'What time is it?'

He glanced at the Rolex on his hair-roughened wrist. 'Six.'

'Really?' She was genuinely shocked. 'I must have got carried away in the kitchen...!'

'The little *hausfrau*,' he drawled, his smile barbed.

'I like to keep busy.' She walked to the fire, aware of his grey eyes on her body. 'I'm bored now, though. I wish there was something to do.'

'You could always dust and hoover,' he said tightly. 'It won't get a proposal of marriage out of me, but it'll certainly convince you that you did your best.'

Caroline gave an angry laugh, hating him. 'You really think I can't wait to marry you, don't you?'

'You're not the first woman to have used that trick on me, Caroline. My instinct for that kind of danger is finely honed, and——'

'Is that how you feel about domesticity, Mark?' She stared at him, her gold-brown hair gleaming like silk in the firelight. 'That it's dangerous?'

'Men don't want marriage,' he said with a hard smile. 'I'm a man. QED.'

'Why don't you want to get married?' she asked softly, suddenly, her heart beating faster as she concentrated on looking into the flames of that fire blazing in the grate.

'Don't ask stupid questions,' he said, eyes narrowing.

'What's stupid about it?' she asked softly, studying the fire. 'I'm just making polite conversation. If you'd rather argue, I'll——'

'All right,' he cut in tightly. 'Polite conversation about marriage! It benefits women, not men.'

'Not according to extensive research,' she murmured. 'Quite the reverse, in fact.'

'I suppose you're going to quote boring statistics at me now.' He laughed. 'Please don't bother. I'm only too well aware of your capacity for twisting the facts to your advantage.'

'And what about you?' she asked, turning her head slowly, fixing him with her green eyes and meeting that suddenly dangerous stare. 'What facts are you twisting here?'

'I'm not twisting anything,' he said in a warning voice.

'I think you are,' she said, her heart beating faster.

He gave a slow dangerous smile. 'Really? Why should you think that?'

'Because you have a very good personal reason for not wanting to get married, and it's coloured your whole life,' she said under her breath, and felt the air between them prickle.

A second later, Mark was sliding off the couch, his hard body straightening as he walked towards her, his eyes predatory, and she could not back away.

'You little bitch!' he said under his breath. 'I told you something in the kitchen that I should have kept to myself! It's been going round and round in your head, hasn't it?'

'Round and round,' she agreed huskily, her eyes riveted on his face.

'I can't believe I told you,' he said tightly. 'Can't believe I said it. I've never discussed it with anyone. Least of all a woman!'

Caroline's heart was beating very fast. He was towering over her, and the violence in his grey eyes was exciting to her.

'I'll bet there are twenty thousand questions in that beautiful little head,' Mark said slowly. 'Why not go ahead and ask them?'

She moistened dry lips. 'Would you really answer them, Mark?'

Menace glittered in his eyes. 'Why not? After all, we've come this far, haven't we? Stuck together, alone in this damned cottage, with nothing better to do but talk. Hell—I hate sharing secrets at the best of times, but I've already let the cat out of the bag, haven't I?'

'You don't have to tell me any big secrets, Mark,' she said huskily, watching him through her lashes. 'I'm no secret sharer, either. We can just drop the subject if you like.'

He laughed harshly. 'Very clever. Putting me at my ease. Making me think it's entirely up to me.' His hand shot out, gripped her chin in hard fingers. 'But it wouldn't be the end of it, would it, Caroline? We both know you're eaten up with curiosity.'

'You're right,' she said softly. 'I'm dying to know all about it. But I would drop it if you asked me. I would, Mark.'

His eyes narrowed. 'Ask your damned questions and let's get it over with.'

She hesitated, then said under her breath, 'Tell me about your mother.'

'My mother?' he drawled with a slow, cynical smile. 'Oh, she was very beautiful. Very wilful, too, as beautiful women so frequently are. She married my father because he'd made her pregnant. Six months later, I was born. A little surprise. Some might even say—a mistake.'

'I'm sorry...' she said softly.

'Don't be,' he said flatly, 'it was my destiny. Fate deals the cards and you play them as best you can.' He studied her, his mouth hard. 'At any rate—my mother wasn't keen on motherhood. Or marriage, for that matter. She ran off with my father's best friend when I was a year old.'

Caroline winced. 'How awful...'

'It gets better!' he drawled. 'She decided she wanted me back so there was a big court wrangle. Then she ran away again with some new guy. More court wrangles. I was shunted back and forth while my parents fought like cat and dog over me. I was twelve when it all came to a shuddering halt. My father won final custody of me, and my mother carried on having lovers all over the world until she died last year.' He looked at her, his face tough. 'The funeral was held in Ireland. I went along and stood in the sunlight and tried to remember the last time I'd spoken to her. I couldn't remember, so I had a little too much champagne and shrugged the whole thing off as life's rich tapestry.' He smiled slowly, eyes flickering over her pale face. 'Got what you wanted?'

She was silent for a long time. Then she said, 'No wonder you hate the mention of marriage.'

His eyes narrowed. 'I don't hate the mention of it,' he said flatly. 'I just don't believe in it.'

'Not all marriages end the way your parents' did.'

'I'm aware of that!' he drawled with a hard smile. 'But the truth is that most of them end, sooner or later, and divorce is divorce no matter how you look at it. Everybody always ends up in a bloody mess, and if children are involved it turns into a full-scale horror story.'

'And that's all you have to say on the subject?'

'Basically, yes.' The black brows arched arrogantly.

Caroline's eyes flickered. 'Well, your behaviour towards the women in your life certainly begins to make sense.'

His mouth tightened. 'Meaning?'

'All your love affairs,' she said softly, watching him through her lashes, the urge to provoke suddenly rearing up in her. 'Venetia Blake and her predecessors.'

'Venetia is an adult,' he said tightly. 'She can look after herself.'

Jealousy stung her. 'She is your mistress, then?'

He smiled cynically. 'Jealous, Miss Shaw?'

'I thought we were on first-name terms, Mark,' she murmured, green eyes intense on his hard, handsome face.

'Yes,' he drawled tightly, 'but this conversation is just a little too personal.'

'That's because we're stuck here in this cottage together,' she murmured, pulses leaping. 'Forced to talk to each other. Live together, practically. No office politics here, Mark. We're just a man and a woman, stranded together in a cottage, miles from nowhere, and you can't stand that, can you? Because you're being forced to live with me as though we're married.' She smiled provocatively. 'You know—watching me cook, wash up, clean the house, ask you what you want for dinner and——'

'I have a housekeeper in London,' he cut in sarcastically. 'And one in Hampshire. There's not much difference, is there?'

'There is,' she said softly, 'if you want to go to bed with the woman in question.'

He breathed harshly, his grey eyes furious.

Caroline laughed under her breath. 'And keep getting refused.'

'You're not refusing me,' he said tightly, eyes like steel knives. 'You're refusing yourself!'

'Hardly!' she laughed breathlessly. 'I think we both know I could make love with you any time I wanted.' Her green eyes flared with open mockery, provocation, her heart beating hard as she pushed him to the limit. 'I wouldn't have to do much more than whistle—would I, Mark? You'd come running to the bedroom in ten seconds flat.'

His teeth met. 'I wouldn't touch you now if you went down on your knees and begged me!'

Caroline blew him a kiss.

He sucked in his breath. 'You little bitch,' he said thickly, and then his hands were on her shoulders, dragging her against his taut body, and the impact of touch was like the explosion of release in both of them.

They kissed desperately, violently, their mouths clinging in fierce fusion, and Caroline's hands were thrusting into his black hair, her fingers shaking as she felt him slide his own hands angrily over her body, down to her waist, her hips, clamping her against him.

Intolerably excited, she was shaking in his hard hands as he kissed her ruthlessly, and she gave him that emotion back, matched it with hunger, crying out hoarsely as she felt his hands move to her breasts, clamping them angrily, his hands hard on her erect nipples.

She whispered fiercely against his mouth, 'Mark...!' Desire blazed in her green eyes, her hands shaking on his strong neck. 'Mark...!'

He stared at her for a second, his heart slamming in his chest.

Then his hands were on her shoulders, dragging her across the room.

He flung her on to the couch with a hoarse sound, eyes blazing as he joined her, pushing her back into the cushions, his strong body covering hers as he arched above her.

'I won't let you take me!' she whispered, her hands stroking his hard-muscled chest.

'The hell you won't!' he bit out thickly, and thrust one hard thigh between hers, making her gasp and close her eyes, whispering his name. 'You provoked this, you little bitch!' Mark said against her mouth. 'Admit it!'

She was kissing him, lingeringly, her pulses throbbing out of control. 'Yes...I provoked it...out of fury...'

'And desire!' he said against her mouth. 'Say it...'

Her green eyes opened, blazing and she whispered fiercely, 'Yes! Desire, too!'

He gave a hoarse groan, and then his mouth was on hers, kissing her into oblivion, and she kissed him back, her hands running over his strong neck, the powerful shoulders, and heard him whisper her name fiercely, his hands moving to the zip of her dress, tugging it down, pulling it roughly from her shoulders to expose her full, firm breasts in the black lacy bra.

He stared down at them for a second, eyes silver with desire and anger, then he made a rough sound of excitement under his breath, his fingers tugging down the lacy bra cups to expose her.

They stared into each other's eyes, both breathing hoarsely as his fingers stroked her bare breasts.

'If I made love to you now,' he said thickly, 'nobody would know. Just you and I. It would be ecstasy, Caroline. We both know it. Lie back and let it happen.' His fingers moved back and forth over her erect nipple. 'Oh, God...let it happen...'

Hot colour flooded her excited face. 'No!'

'Why not?' he asked under his breath. 'It's what we both want!'

She pushed at his broad shoulders, angry. 'Just sexual attraction, Mark? Is that all it is? I've felt it a hundred times before! I can walk away from it without batting an eyelid!'

He met her angry eyes. There was a long fraught silence.

'All right!' he said tightly. 'There's more to it than that and we both know it!'

'Then put a name on it!' she said, her voice shaking. 'Or wave goodbye to it!'

'A name...' He stared, then his face darkened with rage. 'What the hell are you talking about? I want to go to bed with you! It's as simple as that!'

'Still just sex, then?' she said in a hoarse voice, hating him.

'What else is it?' he bit out, eyes blazing. 'I've been going slowly mad in that damned office for months! Sitting there dreaming about you, undressing you, wondering what you'd look like naked...'

'Well, dreams don't always come true,' she said hoarsely, her mouth tight with determination.

His eyes glinted, a smile on his hard mouth. 'They do if you fight for them.'

'But you're not prepared to fight for me—are you, Mark?'

'Want to bet?' he drawled smokily, and bent his dark head to kiss her throat.

Shivers of desire ran through her as that hot mouth burnt a trail to her pulse, throbbing beneath his hard lips, and her hands curled with helpless desire in his hair.

'Don't...' she whispered, closing her eyes, loving every second of this torturous pleasure.

He gave a rough, harsh groan and his hands suddenly tugged the skirt of her dress up over her thighs. He was whispering, 'I want you like hell...let me love you!'

Desperate to submit, Caroline had to summon every last vestige of courage, forcing herself to retreat, moving inside herself to a calm sanctuary fuelled by love.

Mark sensed her withdrawal and became more passionate, his mouth moving urgently to hers, forcing her lips apart though she lay calm and still beneath him, her eyes open and staring unseeingly at the ceiling.

He paused, staring at her, breathing harshly. 'Don't do this, Caroline!' he said unsteadily. 'Not again!'

'I'm not going to let you make love to me, Mark,' she said, eyes tightly shut, determination written on her face.

'God!' he bit out hoarsely. 'You provoked this! I wanted to keep my hands off you! I'm not getting trapped into a bloody proposal of marriage by being driven out of my mind with lust while we're here! If you didn't intend to go through with it—why did you provoke this kiss?'

Shame coloured her face. 'I couldn't help it...' she whispered, staring at his hard mouth. 'I won't give in to my baser instincts, but they provoke me, Mark. They provoke me into things I...' She broke off, her eyes blazing with passion. 'Mark, this is an impossible situation for us both. I want you so much but I can't let myself become your mistress!'

He gave a rough sound of excitement, kissing her. 'Let yourself do what your body wants...' he said thickly. 'Oh God, Caroline, let me love you...' His hands were shaking on her breasts, his mouth burning down over hers. 'Yes, yes...!'

'No!' she said fiercely, tears pricking her eyes as she pushed him hard away from her.

He swore savagely, raised himself on his elbows, face dark red. 'I won't marry you!'

'That's OK,' she said hoarsely, hating him. 'I'm already engaged to be married.' She raised her hand, diamond flashing at him. 'See?'

Violence leapt in his eyes. 'Don't ever show me that bloody thing again!' he snarled, then pushed her violently from him and got to his feet, breathing harshly as he stared down at her with glittering eyes. 'And don't provoke another confrontation like that one, Caroline, or I swear to God I'll take you!' His voice grew ragged, his teeth were bared. 'I'll take you.'

She looked away, her lower lip trembling as hot tears stung the back of her eyes and she found herself unable to reply.

Mark swore under his breath, then strode across the room and slammed the door behind him.

CHAPTER SEVEN

SHAKILY, Caroline got to her feet, pulling her dress back up and zipping it. Mark was right. She had provoked that deliberately, and she couldn't understand what had pushed her to do it.

Desire, she thought bitterly, closing her eyes. An intolerable desire that I've been fighting since the day I met him. God, she wanted him to make love to her. The temptation had been keeping her on a knife edge of sexual tension since she first saw his face and hard body. Living here with him in these circumstances was going to drive her right over the edge if she didn't keep a powerful control over her feelings.

She had always known what kind of man he was: a bastard, not the marrying kind. It had never occurred to her to ask why, but now she knew exactly why, and the information was strangely precious to her. He had a deep undercurrent of violence running through him, and it was triggered by the mention of marriage. Whatever his mother had been like, Caroline guessed she had cut a dark vein of hostility in her son during his childhood, and below that vein she was certain she would find the real Mark: the man capable of love, tenderness, fidelity.

She walked to the fire, stared down. Who are you kidding? she asked herself with a bitter laugh. Mark isn't going to change. He'll always be this man. How many times had he said it since they left London? 'I won't marry you...' Not that I want him to marry me, she thought angrily, because I don't. I do want him to make love to me, though, she thought, drawing a shaky breath. Oh, God, he turns me to liquid fire every time he looks at me, kisses me, touches me...it would be the darkest kind of ecstasy to give in and let him take me. It would be fantastic. Her legs shook beneath her just at the thought. Their naked bodies fusing and slamming together. She wanted him so much...so much...

But she would never let him do it. Mark would take her, enjoy her, then leave her. She refused to let that happen—however exciting his touch. She wanted marriage—Mark wanted a mistress. Her eyes blazed with passionate pride. He could just find a mistress elsewhere and forget about making love to her. Surely he had enough women to choose from! Every woman he met seemed to swoon at his feet.

He didn't want her—he just wanted her body. And it wasn't as though he'd tried to hide his true desires, because he had laid them on the line in no uncertain terms when he'd asked her to become his mistress. She could remember every word he'd said, and not one of them had shown any indication that he cared for her at all.

But how could a man want her so much without feeling anything other than lust? It just didn't make sense. Suddenly she thought of her own rampant and uncontrollable desire for him, and her face flooded with heat. I don't feel anything other than attraction for him! she told herself fiercely. Nothing more. Nothing...

She drew in her breath sharply, ran a hand through her gold-brown hair. I certainly don't feel even affection for him. No, not even that, she told herself. She told herself a lot of other things she didn't feel for him, too, reminding herself she loved Stephen, was going to marry Stephen, wanted Stephen to kiss her, make love to her.

But at the end of all the things she told herself lay one thing and one thing only: Mark's hard mouth against hers and his hands on her body, and she was forced to acknowledge how much she wanted to feel it.

She stood deep in thought for a long time. She added more logs to the fire as and when it needed them. Time moved on. She couldn't stop thinking of him, of his complex personality, and her dangerous excitement whenever he was near...

Much later, the door opened.

Turning, she felt her stomach clench with excitement.

Mark stood in the doorway, broodingly attractive, his black hair and silver eyes and powerful body making *frissons* of awareness caress the hair on the back of her neck.

'It's half-past eight,' Mark said, his gaze moving slowly over her body, lingering on her full breasts. 'We ought to eat.' She moved towards him, and he watched her. As she passed him in the doorway she felt a tremor run between them.

They sat in the kitchen by candlelight, and ate a light supper of chicken and mushroom with sweetcorn, half a tin each, with glasses of red wine left over from lunch.

'Do you enjoy cooking?' Mark asked aggressively as he sat at the table and watched her wash up.

'Not particularly,' she admitted with a smile. 'Unless it's for a dinner party. *Boeuf en croute* for ten served in an elegant dining-room.'

'I thought you lived in a flat,' he said, frowning.

She laughed wryly. 'You can still have dinner parties in a flat.'

'It would have to be a penthouse to get ten in an elegant dining-room,' he drawled, arching a black brow.

'True,' Caroline conceded, hands in hot soapy water. 'But my parents had a beautiful house in Hampshire. They had a lot of dinner parties, I frequently played hostess for them.'

'I have a house in Hampshire,' Mark said with a faint smile. 'Where exactly do your parents live?'

'Lived,' she said quietly. 'They're dead now.'

There was a brief silence. The candle flame flickered in the kitchen, the windows faintly steamed, the snow a barely perceptible white blanket outside.

'I'm sorry,' Mark said coolly.

'Don't be.' She shrugged slender shoulders. 'Fate. It plays these little tricks on us all.'

There was another little silence.

Mark drawled sardonically, 'I suppose that's how you see your meeting with the plastics man. An act of fate?'

'Stop calling him the plastics man,' she said coolly, finishing the washing up and flicking her hands before reaching for a tea-towel. 'His name is Stephen.'

'Stephen the plastics man,' he mocked, grey eyes glinting at her.

She turned, mouth tight. 'Just Stephen will do.'

'Rather a pallid-looking guy, isn't he?' Mark commented arrogantly, leaning back in his chair, hands behind his dark, handsome head. 'Tall, thin and tedious. I bet he never pins you to the bed and kisses the life out of you. He doesn't look as though he could pin a carnation in his lapel without making a bloody mess of it.'

'Stephen is a very nice man!' she said coolly, smiling.

'Nice!' He gave a shout of laughter and stood up, strolling arrogantly across the dim-lit kitchen towards her. 'That's another word for boring, isn't it? In woman-speak? And man-speak, too, come to think of it.'

'Rubbish!' she said harshly, staring at his mouth.

'Is it, Caroline?' he asked softly. Deliberately, he towered over her, placed one hard-muscled arm on either side of her, hands flat on the sink, his whole attitude one of sexual threat. 'If I describe a woman as nice, it generally means I don't fancy her.'

'Define fancying someone,' she said unsteadily, and struggled to fight her awareness of him, lifting her head.

His face was very close to hers. 'If I fancy a woman it means I want to take her to bed and make love to her.'

'Love?' she queried, lifting haughty brows.

'Well,' he murmured, smiling sardonically, 'one or two rather more hard-hitting phrases spring to mind, but I prefer to use them in the bedroom.'

'You know exactly what I meant, Mark!'

'You wanted to know what love had to do with it,' he drawled. 'Well, that's my point exactly. I meet women, I want them, I take them to bed. That's the way I live, Caroline. I'm not for sale on the marriage market and I've never been in love in my life.'

'In other words,' she said haughtily, 'they might just as well all be the same woman for all the notice you take of them. Of their thoughts and feelings and personalities.'

'Not at all. I always have relationships with women,' he said with a hard frown. 'It's not just a return trip to the bedroom with me.'

'You have mistresses!' she said coolly. 'Call that a relationship? It's just an extended one-night stand!'

He laughed softly. 'What would you know about one-night stands?'

Hot colour flooded her face and she looked away, her lashes lowering, sweeping the vulnerable curve of her cheek.

Mark watched her bent head. 'Caroline—love is an illusion. So is marriage. They're lies people tell themselves so they can cope with reality.'

'I can't wait to hear your definition of reality!'

'Sexual attraction,' he said flatly. 'That's all there is between men and women.'

'You're only saying that because of the way your parents——'

'No,' he cut in, his voice cool and very deep as his eyes remained fastened on her face. 'I'm saying it because it's the way it is. Why do you think men have so many affairs? Notice women on the street, flirt with them, admire them—even when they're with their wives. Because they're basically sexual.'

She lifted her head, eyes angry. 'Then why do they bother to get married in the first place?'

'Because they get badgered into it,' he drawled cynically.

'No,' she said flatly. 'Because they fall in love, Mark.'

'You're kidding yourself, Caroline,' he said gently, smiling. 'If anything, marriage is just a way to keep a mistress without the privilege of freedom!'

'Freedom!' she laughed angrily. 'Freedom for the man, you mean! But what about the mistress, Mark? What kind of freedom has she got?'

'The same as the man,' he said with a broad shrug. 'Sexual freedom.'

'We get that in marriage, Mark!' she said sweetly, smiling and looking at him provocatively through her lashes.

His eyes narrowed. 'Some do, but you won't. Not with the plastics man.'

Fury shot through her. 'Oh, yes, I will! Stephen and I——'

'Never kiss,' he drawled mockingly. 'And when you do it doesn't exactly set the world on fire.'

Her face went scarlet. 'That's not true! We kiss all the time!'

'Then why did you go up in flames when I got you on the couch that first night?' he asked under his breath.

'I didn't!' she denied hotly, staring at his hard mouth.

His eyes hardened. 'Don't lie to me—or to yourself.'

Caroline lowered her lashes, the silence suddenly electrifying, and her heart was beating very fast as she realised there was nowhere for her to run to. Not only was he blocking her path with his very powerful body, but they were stuck here together with no way out.

'You want me,' Mark said deeply, watching her bent head. 'You've wanted me from the word go. You've been holding me off for months and playing mummies and daddies with that boy. Your heart's not in it. Your body certainly isn't. You're violently attracted to me—why the hell won't you admit it?'

'I have admitted it,' she said uncertainly. 'I've just refused to act on it. That's all.'

His mouth tightened. 'Because you're going to marry Daly?'

She said nothing, staring through her lashes at his chest, her mouth dry with longing. He was so damned exciting. How was she supposed to resist such intolerable temptation? If only they could get out of this cottage.

Mark thrust a hand under her chin, forced her head up. 'Is that why you keep refusing me, Caroline?' he asked softly.

'I love Stephen. He'll make a perfect husband,' she replied through dry lips, her heart hammering.

The grey eyes flared. 'Without making love to you? Come off it! What do you think marriage is? You'll be living with the man, sharing a bed with him. If he doesn't turn you on—what hope have you got of making it last?'

'I didn't say he didn't turn me on!'

'You didn't need to! It's blatantly obvious that he doesn't raise a glimmer of excitement in you!'

'Because I responded to you?' she snapped heatedly.

'Yes!' he said softly. 'If you'd been passionately involved with Daly, you wouldn't have done it. You certainly wouldn't have spent the last eight months looking at me the way you have done.'

Hot colour flooded her face. 'I don't look at you in any——'

'You look at me continually,' he said under his breath, 'as though you want me to kiss you, touch you, undress you and make love to you.'

'No...' she whispered, closing her eyes.

'And that's exactly what you do want,' he said under his breath, his hand jerking her chin, making her open her eyes and look at his formidable face. 'Isn't it, Caroline? Isn't it?'

Her mouth shook and she said bitterly, 'There's more to life than just sex, Mark!'

'And there's more to life than marriage!'

There was a silence fraught with unbearable tension. The wind howled outside and the candle flames flickered, casting eerie shadows around the room as she stared into his hard, handsome face and felt her legs go weak with the longing to give in...let him take her...oh, God, how much more of this could she stand?

Intolerably confused, she pushed at his broad shoulders, but he wouldn't budge, and she was no match for his strength, feeling quite tiny in front of him, darting quick, uncertain looks up at his tough face.

'You're making me feel claustrophobic!' she said in a shaking voice, her hands curling helplessly on his shoulders. 'Please stop this, Mark. I can't...'

'And you're making me feel seven shades of hellish frustration,' he said thickly, his body pressing against hers suddenly to keep her in place. 'I've made my advance on you, set out my proposition, and accepted your refusal. All well and good. But now I find myself stuck here in this bloody cottage with you for God knows how long and I don't see how I'm going to keep my hands off you.'

'You have a choice, Mark! You don't have to let your body——'

'How the hell would you know?' he drawled. 'You don't have the same kind of body.'

Scarlet colour invaded her cheeks. 'Oh...!'

He gave a sardonic laugh, studying her mouth and murmuring, 'What did you think I was trying to tell you? That I had an overpowering urge to bring you flowers and read you love poems? I have an overpowering urge, all right, but it's not located in——'

'Yes, all right,' she said hoarsely, face scarlet. 'I—I do see.'

He bent his dark head, kissing her mouth. 'I want to make love to you, Caroline.'

'I know...' she whispered, closing her eyes as desire swept through her blood like liquid fire. 'Oh, God...don't kiss me. You'll make it worse for us both.'

He drew in his breath, his strong hands moving to her waist. 'If you were any other woman, this wouldn't be such hell,' he said thickly, his mouth burning torment-ingly, slowly against hers. 'But you're Caroline Shaw, and I've had a thing about you for months.'

She gave a shaky laugh, her hands moving to his dark hair. 'You'd want to make love to me in these circum-stances—whoever I was.'

'I might try,' he drawled lazily, arching black brows. 'But I wouldn't be bothered enough to keep pushing like this.'

'You're a bastard where women are concerned,' she said tensely. 'I should know—I've worked for you for eight months and seen you in action!'

His eyes narrowed. 'Is that why you keep giving me the hands-off treatment?'

'Of course it is!' she said angrily. 'I want a man I can marry—someone like Stephen. A man who——'

'Oh, for God's sake!' he snapped, eyes suddenly blazing and his hands tightening painfully on her waist. 'If you say "marry" one more time I'll——'

'Well, what's wrong with it?' she said fiercely. 'You stand here and tell me I should understand how you feel because your——' Her face flamed. 'Because your body makes life uncomfortable for you when you're severely aroused, yet you refuse to even consider my feelings about love and marriage!'

'Love isn't a part of marriage and never has been!'

'It's not a part of casual sex, either!'

His teeth met. 'By the time I get you into bed, Caroline, it's not going to feel remotely casual!'

'You'll never get me into bed!' she said fiercely. 'And you'd save us both a great deal of trouble if you just stopped trying, Mark, because I don't want it to happen and I——'

'Is that so?' he said softly, and suddenly jerked her hard against his body.

She gave a smothered gasp of excitement, her heart beating with abrupt violence at the sudden contact with his hard thighs, powerful chest, her hands shaking on his shoulders as she stared up into his handsome face and her mouth went dry with longing.

'Well, come on—what are you waiting for?' he said thickly, his eyes glittering in his angry face. 'Push me away... tell me not to kiss you...'

She just stared at his mouth, unable to speak.

'You can't do it, can you?' he said under his breath. 'When we're this close your body takes over. Doesn't it, Caroline?'

Her eyes closed briefly and her dry mouth said in tortured honesty, 'Yes!' and as she opened her eyes the expression she saw on his face made her give a silent moan, and a second later his mouth was meeting hers.

The kiss was so unbearably sensual that she was lost in seconds, her mouth opening beneath his in dizzying response, and his hands stroked her hair as the kiss deepened, sending her spinning into absolute desire, her hands moving shakily to his strong neck, running slowly over the warm skin, into his black hair.

The thud of his heart and the slow tenderness of his hands sent her into delirium, moaning softly as she felt him slide them up to cup her breasts, and as he stroked her erect nipples she kissed him back with slow, hot urgency, her heart slamming until her whole body shook with desire.

Suddenly, she was struggling out of that intoxicating embrace. 'Don't . . . !'

He drew a ragged breath, lifting his head. 'Caroline, you need this,' he said urgently, holding her with possessive hands. 'You're going crazy with frustration. Let me ease it . . . let me make love to you . . .'

Rage and sudden pain shot through her and she cried bitterly, 'Don't ever use that phrase again, Mark! Not ever, do you understand me? You don't mean a damned word of it, and you never will!' Tears suddenly burnt the back of her eyes for no accountable reason and her voice grew hoarse. 'You're a phoney bastard! You treat women abominably and justify it to yourself on the grounds that you're a man and therefore entitled to have sex with any woman you fancy on whatever terms you're prepared to give!'

'I don't!' he bit out thickly, but his face ran with dark colour.

'Oh, yes, you do! And you've been doing it all your life because the women you've met have been too much in love with you to deny your selfish and hurtful requests! You don't care about anything but yourself,' she said hoarsely. 'And I do. I care about a lot of things, Mark. I don't want an empty life with no love and no one to turn to when I'm old. And that's what you're offering me.' Her eyes were stinging with tears. 'Isn't it, Mark? You're offering me loneliness and regret and self-hatred.'

'No,' he said slowly, staring, but there was shock in his eyes.

'It is, Mark,' she said thickly, and pushed him away from her, her mouth trembling as the tears threatened to spill. 'Whereas Stephen is offering me love, friendship, support, commitment, loyalty and a future that contains children.'

Mark let her go, but followed her with angry eyes and said harshly, 'But you don't want to make love with him!'

She stopped and looked back at him, her face tight with anger. 'Don't I, Mark?' she asked softly. 'What makes you think that?'

His face tightened. 'Your response when——'

'Well, if you can fancy more than one woman at a time,' she said under her breath, 'I can fancy more than one man. Don't you think?'

He sucked in his breath, eyes furious. 'I don't believe it!'

'That,' she said through tight lips, 'is not my problem.' Giving him a slow, anger-fuelled smile, she went out of the kitchen, closing the door behind her.

She went into the living-room and sat down, trembling with anger. That had told him! Well—why should she admit that Stephen's kisses incited nothing more than warmth and affection?

Half an hour later, Mark came into the room, glowering at her. 'I'm going to have a glass of whisky and then go to bed,' he said tightly, striding across to the drinks cabinet. 'Do you want anything to drink?'

Caroline watched him through her lashes. 'Hot chocolate?'

'Forget it,' he snapped, unscrewing the whisky bottle. 'I'm not some damned domesticated little wimp.'

'You're not very friendly, either,' she said with a suppressed smile.

His mouth tightened. 'I'll pour you a glass of whisky, but I'm not making you hot chocolate.'

'No, I'm sure it would be far too demanding for your male ego.'

'Damn right.' He raised the whisky glass to his hard mouth.

Caroline slid off the couch with a sigh. 'I'll have to go and make it myself, then, won't I?'

His eyes narrowed as he watched her pad across the room. 'Don't try to make me feel guilty, because it won't work.'

'Who's trying to make you feel guilty?' she asked coolly, looking back over one slender shoulder, her gold-brown hair sliding in silky disarray across one green eye.

'I'm sure the plastics man would have leapt to the saucepan,' he drawled disparagingly. 'I bet he would even have cooked the dinner.'

'But that's what I like about Stephen,' she said softly, 'he's so thoughtful and unselfish.' Going out of the room, she smiled at the memory of his furious face as she went into the kitchen and made herself a cup of hot chocolate with boiling water as there was no milk.

When she went back into the living-room, Mark was drinking another small measure of whisky. 'I notice the snow is still falling,' she said. 'Until it stops, we don't stand a chance of rescue.'

'The sooner we get out of this bloody place the better,' he said, his voice hard.

They sat in unfriendly silence for a long time. When Caroline had finished her hot chocolate, she said, 'I'll go upstairs and make the beds. I'm sure putting sheets on a bed would be beneath your male dignity, too.'

His eyes narrowed. 'I'm quite capable of any domestic chore you can come up with. I just prefer to pay other people to do them.'

'I'm afraid there aren't any professional cleaners in the house with us,' she said sarcastically. 'So we'll just have to share the work.'

'God, you're such a bitch!' he said disagreeably, and drank some whisky.

'And you, Mark, are a total pig.'

He slammed the whisky down. 'Look! I just don't like being in a situation where——'

'You feel married,' she murmured, walking to the door with a lit candle. 'Yes, I quite understand, Mark.'

She went upstairs. It was icy cold, and her breath froze in front of her. Walking into the front bedroom, she glanced around, satisfied at the small double bed with thick duvet and the fireplace with coal and logs beside it. Then she went into the back bedroom, and froze with horror. It wasn't a bedroom at all. It was something of a junk shop, with objects piled high in messy clutter.

Panic hit her. She went back into the front bedroom, staring around. Then she heard his footsteps on the stairs. Breathless, she turned, her face pale against the candle flame as she stared at the doorway of the bedroom and watched him walk in.

'Which room is mine?' Mark asked flatly. 'I'll make my own bed.'

She swallowed. 'There's only one bed and one duvet, Mark.'

A muscle jerked in his cheek. Silent, he turned on his heel and walked into the other bedroom, and there was a tense silence, then he returned, his eyes very dark.

'I'll sleep downstairs on the couch,' he said tautly. 'Under both our coats. The fire will keep me from freezing to death.'

'No, it won't,' she said huskily. 'Look at the air in here...' She breathed, her breath misting icily in front of her. 'The fire will go out while you're asleep. You might die of cold in the night.'

He raked a hand through his hair. 'You're right.'

There was a brief silence, and her heart was banging so hard she felt sure he must hear it.

'We can keep our clothes on,' Caroline suggested.

He looked at her, his eyes dangerous. 'I think that's advisable!'

Her heart slammed harder. 'Well...' Her voice was shaking. 'We'd better light the fire, hadn't we?'

'I'll do it,' he said tightly, moving into the room. 'You get into bed and try to fall asleep as fast as possible.'

She watched him, ravishing by candlelight.

'Get into bed, Caroline!' he said flatly.

She moved to the bed at once, putting the candle on the night table and sliding in between that icy duvet and the icy sheet.

Mark worked on the fire for a long time, putting coal and logs in the grate, lighting the small white firelighter in the centre, and waiting in tense silence for the blaze to start attacking the fuel.

Caroline tried desperately to fall asleep, but of course she couldn't and when Mark finally came to bed half an hour later she was lying there, her heart drumming and her mouth as dry as ashes.

He slid in beside her, and their bodies brushed. Keeping her eyes tightly shut, she feigned sleep, but her breathing betrayed her, erratic and unsteady as that loud banging heart shook her body.

'I know you're awake, Caroline.'

'Pretend I'm asleep,' she whispered hoarsely.

He could feel her heart slamming. 'Open your eyes, Caroline!' he said thickly.

With intense dread, she opened her eyes, and there he was, his dark head on the pillow beside her, and as she looked into his hard face she felt as though they had been moving towards this moment forever.

'Put your arms around me.' He was breathing hard, his eyes silver, and she stared at him, her face pale.

'Mark...'

'We have to sleep close or we'll die,' he said harshly. 'Now just do it, will you?'

Breathing erratically, Caroline slid against his hard body. Her arms went around his powerful chest. Their legs slowly twined together. Excitement was shooting through her like pure adrenalin, and she tried to lie still, not feel aroused, but her face was against his dark throat and she could taste the scent of his skin, feel the warmth of the muscles below that black cashmere sweater.

The banging of their hearts was suddenly intolerable to her. She lifted her face to him with a hoarse moan, and heard his rough sound of answering hunger as his head swooped.

Their mouths met with fierce need, and he was pushing her on to her back, making harsh sounds of excitement as he kissed her into the pillows, his hands moving over her body, while she melted beneath him, desire pulsating like fire through her veins.

Her hands were in his thick black hair, her mouth open passionately beneath his, and the kiss blazed on while his strong hands moved over her breasts, stroking her erect nipples, then moving slowly, inexorably, temptingly to her slender thighs.

'Oh, God...!' Mark breathed harshly, rapidly, and the kiss deepened as his hands began to stroke her skirt upwards to expose her long slim thighs. 'I need you!' he said thickly against her mouth. 'I want to love you... Caroline...' His hands moved slowly, sensually over her slim thighs. 'We're in bed together, my darling. Let me take you...'

'Words of love, Mark,' she whispered thickly against his black hair, 'with no real emotion behind them.'

'Of course there's emotion behind them,' he said unsteadily, his mouth moving back to meet hers, kissing her lingeringly, torturously. 'But it's not love. I'll be as honest as I have been from the beginning. I'm not in love with you and I never will be.' His grey eyes stared burningly down at her flushed face. 'But I want to make love to you so damned much...'

'Well, you can't,' she said as pain shot through her heart and her face was tight with it, eyes dark with it. Suddenly, she found the strength to push him hard away from her. 'I don't want any part of your phoney declarations—or your horribly phoney lifestyle! If you want a mistress, you can find one elsewhere.'

His eyes blazed fierce silver in his darkly flushed face. 'Not tonight, I bloody well can't!'

The pain in her heart increased. 'That just shows how phoney you really are, Mark! Your declarations of driven passion are just a way to amuse yourself while you're snowbound with a woman. And if you think that's going to make me give in with sighs of ecstasy, you're in for a big surprise!' Angrily, she pushed at his broad shoulders. 'Kindly get off me, Mark. I want to go to sleep.'

He stared down at her in furious silence for a long moment, his face darkly flushed and his mouth shaking with barely suppressed rage. 'You bitch!' he swore hoarsely.

'Oh, that's your answer to everything, isn't it?' she snapped furiously. 'When you can't get what you want from a woman, you turn around and call her a bitch! You're like a little boy, Mark! When will you learn that you can't have everything you want?'

Rage leapt in his eyes. He swore savagely, his hands tangling in her hair, hurting her deliberately as he tugged her head back.

'Oh!' Tears sprang to her eyes and she said bitterly, 'That's right! Having failed with insults and seductive persuasion, you now graduate to physical violence! Very impressive, Mark! I can't wait to see your next move!'

He stared down at her, breathing harshly, and she suddenly saw the visible effort he was making to control himself. Suddenly, he pushed her violently from him and got out of bed, saying bitingly, 'I'm going downstairs for some more whisky! I'll come back to bed when I'm damned sure you're asleep, because I sure as hell can't take much more of this frustration, even if you can!'

The door slammed behind him, his footsteps echoing angrily down the stairs. When she heard the living-room door slam, she felt the prick of tears at the back of her eyes.

Well, he'd certainly been honest with her! 'I'm not in love with you and I never will be.' How she hated him! Ruthless, cynical bastard! she thought, tugging the duvet over her shaking shoulders.

She felt so terribly hurt, so rejected and full of hatred for him. But why should she feel that? It was absurd—he was just her boss, just a man who wanted to get her into bed, and here she was in tears because she had once again refused him.

But that wasn't why she felt so desperately hurt and she knew it.

It was because of that brutal statement: 'I'm not in love with you and I never will be.' But why should that be painful to hear and to accept? After all—she wasn't in love with him either. In fact, she couldn't care less if she never saw him again after this weekend.

Could she...?

CHAPTER EIGHT

WHEN Caroline woke up the next morning, she was in Mark's arms. During the night, as they both slept and the room became icy cold, they had moved together, holding each other close for warmth.

Now her face was cradled against his powerful chest, and she could feel his heart beating steadily against her skin. His breath fanned the top of her gold-brown head. His arms were around her, their legs tangled together, the duvet warm and snug on top of them.

Birds were singing. Caroline frowned, lifting her head. That must mean the snow had stopped!

'Mmm...' Mark murmured drowsily as she moved, and held her closer, his mouth absently kissing the top of her head. 'Caroline...'

She felt her heart miss a beat, and looked up at him through her lashes.

He was still asleep, his eyes closed. If anything, the brute looked even more handsome. Those thick black lashes flickered on hard cheekbones and his black hair was tousled, softening his tough good looks with heart-stopping appeal.

Caroline's mouth twisted in an irritated smile. He's gorgeous, she thought, hating him for being so attractive. Of course—that was another reason why he behaved like such a bastard to women. He got away with it. With those looks, what woman could resist him?

Rugged face, wicked mind, sexy eyes, powerful body, impressive height—and he was wealthy too, damn him.

'I can resist you, Mark Rider,' she murmured, and then bent her head, her mouth brushing his softly.

His eyes opened.

Caroline gasped, staring, her mouth against his, then tried to draw away.

'No, you don't!' he said, arms tightening around her, pressing her close to him. 'That was a very enjoyable good morning kiss. I want another one.'

'Well, you can't have one!' she said huskily, trying to wriggle away from him.

'What did you mean by saying you could resist me?' he drawled softly, holding her easily.

'What do you think I meant?' Her heart was skipping beats, her body lying helpless on top of his, and the throb of excitement was already stirring in her blood.

'That you're having quite a struggle,' he mocked under his breath, grey eyes gleaming.

Hot colour flooded her face. She was so intensely aware of him, his body against her and his strong face so close. His jaw was dark with stubble. His black hair sleep-tousled. He made her heart miss beats just to look at him.

'You're beautiful first thing in the morning,' he said softly, a smile on his hard mouth as he studied her. 'Your skin's so soft, your hair so silky. I like finding you on my pillow. We must do it more often.'

'How many times do I have to tell you?' she said huskily. 'I want love...marriage...Stephen...'

'Stephen's last on the list, though,' he said. 'Don't you think that's the road to divorce?'

'I'll never divorce,' she said softly. 'That's another reason I won't let you near me. Loyalty, remember? Loyalty, trust, reliability and affection.'

'You could always buy a dog and call it Stephen,' he drawled in cruel mockery.

'I'll pretend I didn't hear that,' she said tightly. 'If I did hear it, I might just have to slap your face.'

'Don't slap my face.' Suddenly, he pushed her on to her back, arching above her, his powerful body deeply exciting as it slid against hers. 'Just kiss me, darling...' His warm mouth sought hers, a rough sigh in his throat as he kissed her slowly, sensually, his hands moving down over her body and making her respond instantly.

'No!' Caroline said shakily, jerking her face from his. 'I don't want this!'

'Yes, you do!' he said against her mouth. 'Oh, yes, Caroline, you——'

'No, Mark, I don't!' she said fiercely. 'But you won't take no for an answer, will you? Your ego can't face the fact that I'm rejecting what you think is such a fantastic offer! To be used by a bastard like you, then dumped the minute you're bored with me!'

'It's not like that!' he said impatiently.

'Oh, yes, it is! But I won't get involved with you— on this or any other level, and the sooner you accept that the better!'

'I have accepted it!' he bit out savagely. 'I just find myself stranded here with you. Why shouldn't I try to get you into bed? I always fancy sex first thing in the morning. But if you don't want to give it to me, that's fine with me. I shall get it from Venetia Blake just as soon as we get back to London!' He got off the bed, his face a dark mask of rage, then strode across the bedroom, slamming the door so hard that it rattled on its hinges.

She lay in bed, her face white, green eyes flaring with jealousy. The thought of Mark making love to that black-haired witch was almost a physical blow. Why should I care? she thought fiercely. Let him do what he likes. I don't want him. I shall go back to my ordinary life, marry Stephen, settle down and have children.

She heard the shower going in the bathroom and realised Mark would be some time. Hardly surprising. It wasn't much fun sleeping in one's clothes. She was dying for a shower, too.

The kitchen was icy. Caroline switched all the gas jets on and busied herself making breakfast. She made a breakfast of assorted fruits; tinned raspberries, peaches and pineapple.

'The bathroom is free,' Mark said disagreeably when he came into the kitchen, drying his wet black hair with a towel. 'I found some toothpaste and a toothbrush. There are clean towels in the bathroom cupboard.'

'I'll go up and take a shower, then,' she said coolly, brows lifting. 'I made breakfast. I thought fruit would be pleasant.'

'You do have initiative, then,' he said nastily. 'I might even remember why I hired you as my secretary.'

'Not just a decision made below the waist, then?' she asked tightly.

His eyes narrowed. 'I hired you for your professional skills.'

'And now you're trying to teach me new professional skills,' she couldn't resist saying, her eyes flaring with sudden anger and hurt.

Mark was silent for a long time, the bones in his face seeming to push out from beneath his tanned skin. Black rage darkened his steel-grey eyes. He looked as though he wanted to hit her.

'I'll go and take my shower.' Caroline tried to move past him.

He blocked her path. 'Apologise!' he said thickly.

She looked up into his dark face. 'What?'

'I said apologise, you little bitch!' he bit out under his breath, and his hand gripped her arm tightly. 'What are you—deaf?'

She tried to wrench her arm free. 'Why should I apologise for telling you the truth?'

'It isn't the truth!' he said between his teeth. 'It was a genuine offer, and it wasn't lightly made.'

She laughed. '"Sincere, genuine guy seeks paid whore"? Oh, I can just see it in the personal columns.'

'I never at any time——'

'Yes, you did!'

He breathed harshly, eyes glittering. 'It seemed the best solution to an attraction that was going nowhere but getting stronger. What the hell was I supposed to do? Just stand back and let it carry on forever?'

'Hardly forever!' she said scathingly. 'I've just got engaged—remember?' She lifted her left hand, the diamond flashing in the light. 'I'll be getting married soon and——'

'Married!' His fingers bit into her wrist. 'The hell you will! You're not in love with that guy! You don't even fancy him!' The grey eyes flared violently. 'And before you remind me of last night, let me tell you I don't believe a word of what you said!'

'Oh, no?' she blustered, face flushing furiously.

'No!' His upper lip curled back in a sneer. 'When I saw you dance with him at the Ritz, I knew you were making a mistake. You might just as well have been dancing with your oldest teddy bear as with a man!'

Her mouth tightened. 'People keep teddy bears forever.'

'Children,' he said flatly, eyes hard. 'Not adult women.'

Caroline glared at him for a moment, then tried to wrench her arm out of his grip. He refused to let go.

'Got to you then, did I?' he drawled, eyes narrowed.

'Not at all,' she said icily, and tried to move past him.

'You can't keep ending these conversations, Caroline!' he said thickly. 'You've been doing it in the office for months. This attraction hasn't stopped. It's just got stronger. Why won't you at least sit down and talk about it?'

'Because,' she said unsteadily, 'I want to go upstairs and take a shower.'

'Not go upstairs and hide?' he said angrily.

She wrenched her arm free. 'Why should I need to hide? Nothing you've said has been true. I still love Stephen, still intend to marry him, and nothing you can say or do will change my mind.' Before he could stop her, she escaped, and ran upstairs.

It was unbearably cold. The water was even colder. Caroline stood under the stinging icy shower with her teeth chattering and goose-bumps mottling her usually soft, silken skin. Washing her hair was agony, but she did it, groaning at the cold, and was very glad to wrap herself in a fluffy bath-towel later and rub her icy scalp warm again with a hand-towel.

Putting the same clothes back on wasn't as bad as she'd expected it to be. At least her skin and hair were clean.

Mark was out in the front garden when she got downstairs.

'Hang on!' she called in sudden hoarse alarm, quickly going to the doorway and looking out at the sunlit snow-bound land. 'You're not going, are you?'

He looked back, grey eyes scanning her white, frightened face. 'I'm just off to check on the Bentley,' he said slowly, frowning. 'What did you think I was doing? Leaving you stranded here?'

She flushed hotly, panic subsiding. 'I—I wasn't sure.'

'I must admit I'm tempted,' he said between his teeth. 'You're hardly my ideal woman to get snowbound with.'

'Well, you're hardly my ideal man!' she said, prickling angrily.

He smiled unpleasantly. 'And what would Daly do if he was here with you? Sit you on a pink cushion and peel grapes for you?'

'At least he wouldn't keep trying to peel my clothes off!' she snapped, then went scarlet, jerking her face away, furious with herself.

A nasty gleam entered Mark's eyes. 'I thought you found him unbearably attractive?' he drawled mockingly. 'I thought he was the——'

'I thought you were going to check on the Bentley?' she cut in acidly.

He met her furious eyes and laughed under his breath, looking very formidable and sexy in the black cashmere coat, every inch the dangerous seducer of women. 'Yes, I am. Why not come with me?'

'In high heels?' she asked scornfully.

'I found some boots in the cupboard under the stairs. There are several pairs. Try one on and get back to me.'

Caroline drew a level breath, then moved away from the icy cold doorway. At least he hadn't tried to pursue that particular line of enquiry further. The last thing she wanted him to know was that Stephen had never made any attempt to make love to her.

She found a pair of boots that almost fitted, and trudged out to him.

'*Très elegante*,' he drawled, studying her slim legs below her coat thrust into thick black over-sized wellington boots.

'Oh, shut up,' she snapped irritably, and trudged past him, her feet sinking deeply into the crisp white snow. 'This must be at least six inches deep!'

'And about to thaw,' he remarked, gesturing to the sun struggling through wintry white clouds. They trudged down to the road. 'That snowdrift is the Bentley,' he said wryly. 'I'll clear the snow off it, try to start it. If nothing else, I'll be able to figure out what's wrong with it.'

'It crashed into a brick wall,' Caroline said, 'that's what's wrong with it.'

He smiled sardonically, eyes gleaming. 'Temper, temper!'

'I'm not in a temper,' she said, lifting her gold-brown head. 'Just irritated to be stranded here with you.'

He laughed softly. 'I really am getting to you, aren't I? What happened to the cool, controlled Miss Shaw I knew last week? The one who never got into personal conversations, refused all my invitations, slid out of the office night after night with a secret, seductive little smile on her face?'

Tensing, she said flatly, 'There's nothing different about me here!'

'Oh, yes, there, is,' he said, considering her thoughtfully. 'That's why we're permanently arguing. Because you don't like being trapped in such close proximity with me any more than I like it.'

'Rubbish!' she said huskily, trying to move away.

His hand caught her arm, eyes narrowed on her intently. 'You ran out of the kitchen earlier, when I started this conversation.'

'I did not run!'

'Yes, you did,' he said under his breath. 'Just as you've been running from me at the office. Well, we're stuck here together now, and there's nowhere left to run. That's what's bothering you most, isn't it? It's not just the sexual temptation we're both having to fight, it's——'

'I thought we were going to see the Bentley!' she snapped, heart thudding too fast.

'You really hate me being this close, don't you?' he said, eyes narrowed. 'I'm too close. And you can't keep up that front any more, can you? Cool, controlled little Miss Shaw is disintegrating right in front of my eyes. And who's taking her place?' He stared, his face very close. 'A very passionate, emotional, tempestuous woman.'

'Let go of me!' she said furiously, trying to pull herself free.

'A woman who wants me as much as I want her,' he said deeply. 'So why won't you let me take you? It's not just sex that you're afraid of. Is it? There's more. You're afraid to be yourself with me and——'

'Shut up!' she said unsteadily, and wrenched herself free.

It went wrong. She fell over with the force of her movement, giving a cry of sheer agony as her right foot remained stuck in the snow while her body fell at a very awkward angle.

Mark caught her before she hit the ground, his strong hands shooting out to grab her waist.

'Oh, God!' she moaned in agony and clutched his shoulders with nerveless fingers. 'My ankle...'

'Is it broken...?' he demanded, holding her.

'I don't know!' she groaned. 'I didn't feel the bone snap, but it's agony...Mark...I can't stand on it!'

'You obstinate little fool! If you hadn't been so intent on running away again——' His mouth bit back the words, eyes flaring furious silver. Then he swore under his breath, scooped her up into his powerful arms and trudged back to the house with her while she clung to his neck, wincing at the needles of pain shooting continually through her right ankle.

Swinging her into the living-room, he deposited her on the couch. The fire was crackling away. He must have lit it while she was taking her icy shower.

'Where does it hurt?' he demanded harshly, pulling off her boots.

'My right ankle...' she mumbled, lifting her right leg fractionally off the couch.

He touched her ankle with long fingers.

'Ow!' Caroline flinched from the pain.

'I have to feel for a break,' he said deeply, grimacing, and was more gentle as he pressed the bone.

'It hurts!' she whispered, biting her lip.

'I can see it hurts,' he drawled. 'But there's very little I can do about that. You'll just have to be brave.'

She obeyed, wincing, her fingers gripping the edge of the cushions. She was tempted to pick up a small cushion and bite into it to stop herself crying out with pain.

'It's just a sprain,' Mark said eventually. 'A nasty one, though. I can see the bruise coming up already.'

'Oh, no!' she groaned, eyes closing. 'That's all I need! How am I going to walk to the village with you when the snow melts?'

'You're not,' he said grimly.

She stared, appalled. 'You—you can't leave me here alone! What if someone broke in…I'd never get away…'

'I won't leave you,' he said with an impatient sigh. He straightened, raking a strong hand through his dark hair and looking down at her with those penetrating eyes. 'I'll just have to stay here either until we're rescued, or I fix the car.'

Her panic subsided and she mumbled gratefully, 'Thank you, Mark.'

'Don't mention it,' he drawled. 'And I mean that!' He laughed harshly, then moved towards the door. 'I'll get a basin of warm water for you to put it in. With any luck, that will ease the pain and stop the swelling.'

The door closed behind him. Caroline considered his actions for a long moment in silence, as surprised as she was touched. Then she remembered he would be coming back at any minute, and she gingerly stripped her tights off, groaning in agony as she pulled the right foot off.

He returned a few minutes later with a large red basin of warm water from the kettle and a bathtowel, which he spread on the floor before putting the red basin on it.

'Thanks,' Caroline muttered, sliding her foot into the deliciously warm water and groaning as her ankle throbbed painfully. 'Oh, God...!'

Mark watched her with a frown. 'It's beginning to swell.'

'How very attractive I shall look,' she grimaced.

'Oh, I don't know,' he drawled softly. 'You'll be helpless for the rest of the time we're here. After what I've been through this weekend, I find the thought of Caroline Shaw totally defenceless rather exciting.'

Her mouth dried. She stared down at him. 'You wouldn't...'

'I might,' he drawled, mockery in his smile.

Her pulses leapt and she said lightly, 'I may not be able to run away from you, but I can certainly hobble!'

He laughed and their eyes held for a brief moment. Caroline's heart stopped beating.

Mark's smile slowly faded. He got to his feet, looking down at her broodingly, hands thrust in black trouser pockets. 'I'm going to go and clear the Bentley, take a look at the engine. Will you be all right here?'

She was surprised to find her voice husky. 'I'll be fine.'

He nodded, face hard. 'If you need anything, just shout.'

Caroline said on impulse, 'Thanks. You're being rather kind—for Mark Rider.'

'Anyone would do as much.'

'You're not just anyone,' she said huskily, and there was a peculiar, heart-stopping silence.

Mark was looking at her oddly, and she flushed under that stare, lowering her lashes and feeling deeply self-conscious.

Face burning, she said impatiently, 'I thought you were going to look at the Bentley!'

'I am,' he said slowly, frowning at her, then turned on his heel and strode out.

Caroline gave a sigh of relief as she heard the front door slam after him. At least he hadn't questioned her closely on that remark. She didn't even know the answer to it herself. What *had* she meant, she wondered, by saying Mark Rider wasn't just anyone?

Surely she hadn't meant that she saw him as different from any other man she had ever known? Her heart thudded disturbingly fast. That was exactly what she had meant. He was different. Totally different.

He was darkly exciting, powerful, strong, arrogant, egotistical and he had made every hair on the back of her neck stand on end from the minute she'd first set eyes on him. Of course he was different!

He really isn't just anyone, she thought with a shock…

CHAPTER NINE

CAROLINE spent the following hour flicking unseeingly through magazines. The weekend had turned into an unexpected nightmare in this cottage, and now that she'd sprained her ankle it was even more of a nightmare.

She didn't like all those things Mark had said to her just before she'd hurt herself. He was getting too close to the truth. She didn't want him to know her. Certainly, she didn't want him to know quite how deep her emotions ran. He would take advantage of it, use her passionate nature against her when trouble cropped up between them.

Caroline was a very passionate and emotional woman—that was the trouble. She was afraid to let herself go, particularly with someone like Mark. But how she yearned to...

The sound of the front door slamming made her breathless. She busied herself with her magazines, pretending great interest in an article about time management.

Mark strode into the living-room. He paused in the doorway for a split second, watching her from beneath his heavy eyelids, an odd expression on his dark, brooding face.

'How's the Bentley?' Caroline asked, lifting her head.

'Not in good shape,' he said flatly, hands black with engine oil. 'I found the alternator on the ground below it.'

'Alternator?' She frowned, mystified.

'It's the mechanism that keeps the battery replenishing as you drive,' he explained. 'It was smashed loose by the crash. So were several other fairly vital engine parts. I've fixed them all back into place, but the battery's completely dead.'

'You obviously know your stuff,' she said, not having understood a word of that. 'Why is the battery dead?'

He grimaced. 'Ah. This is where I have to make a confession. I left the lights on.'

She groaned. 'Oh, no...'

He gave a harsh sigh. 'It was because it was an emergency, of course. I forgot the lights were on. All I was concerned about was getting us both to shelter. One reads so many horror stories of people dying in their cars in blizzards...'

She nodded, watching him through her lashes.

The grey eyes flicked down her long slim legs. 'How's your ankle?' he asked abruptly.

'Much better,' she said with some surprise. 'It throbs a lot, and it's still painful, but it's not agonising any more.'

'I'll bandage it up once the swelling has gone down,' he told her. 'Then you can start to limp.'

She laughed, green eyes wryly amused. 'Thank you, Dr Rider.'

He grinned. 'Not at all.' Suddenly, a gleam came into his eyes. 'A pity you're not responding to my bedside manner, though.'

Caroline laughed. 'Poor Dr Rider! Forlorn and unloved!'

His teeth met. 'Are you laughing at me?'

Her pulses skipped. 'I wouldn't dream of it,' she murmured.

'I hope not,' he said under his breath, an edge to his voice. 'I don't need to tell you what kind of retaliation you'll get if you do.'

'No,' she said softly, wary excitement in her eyes. 'It's constantly on my mind.'

He caught his breath audibly, staring.

There was a brief, tense silence.

Caroline cleared her throat, pulses leaping. 'Hadn't you better go and wash you hands, Mark? They're covered in engine oil...'

He watched her in silence for a second, then drawled, 'You have a knack for sliding out of difficult conversations, Miss Shaw. Very well. I'll go and wash my hands. But I'll be back very shortly, and then you and I are going to have that conversation.'

'Which conversation?' she asked huskily, staring.

'You know very well which conversation,' he said, grey eyes penetrating, and then moved out of the room, leaving her to feel very definitely under threat as she sat there, helpless, one foot stuck in a basin of water.

Outside in the kitchen, she could hear him washing his hands. Her heart was jumping. Her mouth was dry. She didn't want to talk to him—certainly not about herself.

He came back, without his coat, and his hard-muscled body sent quivers of awareness through her. He smiled at her lazily, a glitter of sardonic amusement in his grey eyes as he sank down slowly on the couch beside her, and his hard thigh brushed hers.

Caroline shifted, wary excitement in her eyes.

'My, my,' he drawled softly, 'you are jumpy, aren't you?'

'I'm just not in the mood for a chat,' she said flatly.

'Hardly a chat,' he drawled wryly. 'More like a very personal discussion. One you've been avoiding for a long, long time. You got out of it earlier by spraining your ankle. I let it slide because I figured you needed a moment to recover. Well...' he idly stroked her thigh with one long finger ' ... you've had your moment. Now it's time to talk turkey.'

'Look, I don't have to discuss anything with you if I don't want to,' she snapped. 'Not even the weather!'

'Tell me about your relationship with Stephen Daly,' he said suddenly, surprising her.

Her long gold lashes flickered. 'What... ?'

'Your relationship with him,' he said coolly, black brows arching. 'How you get on, what you have in common, the things you talk about, what you do, where you go, the——'

'Yes, all right,' she said irritably. 'I... well, let me see. We get on very well. It's true we don't have much in common, but opposites attract, don't they? We talk about his job, my job, our future together. We go to the theatre a lot, sometimes we——'

'What kind of plays do you go to see?' he asked, unsmiling.

She sighed. 'I've got to humour you, have I?'

He laughed and inclined his dark head. 'All the way.'

'And if I refuse?'

'Then I take you upstairs and start making love to you, Caro,' he said softly, smiling lazily. 'And I don't think you'll find it so easy to end the excitement by running away, because . . . well, you're hardly physically able any more. Are you?'

She flushed deeply, heart thumping, looked away and tried not to betray the wild flare of excitement in her at the thought of being that helpless . . . the choice would be taken away from her and lovemaking would be something she was forced to accept from him. Oh, God, how she wanted to make love with him. It was becoming intolerable . . .

'Your recitation, please,' Mark drawled softly beside her.

She tightened her mouth. 'We go to see the current plays.'

'Anything fashionable, then?' he asked, frowning.

'Yes,' she said shortly, and glared at him.

He was silent for a moment, studying her. Then he said, 'My favourite play is *Cat on a Hot Tin Roof*.'

Her eyes narrowed. 'Is that meant to be a humorous——?'

'I'm merely telling you my favourite play,' he said, smiling lazily. 'What's yours?'

She gave an irritable sigh. '*A Streetcar Named Desire*, I suppose.'

'Why do you like it?' he asked coolly.

Caroline folded her arms, giving him an angry look. 'I fail to see what any of this has to do with——'

'Just answer the question,' he drawled, eyes mocking. 'Or it's upstairs to bed for you.'

Heat flooded her and she said unsteadily. 'I like *Streetcar* because there's a lot of drama, excitement . . .'

He smiled lazily, then said, 'What's Stephen's favourite play?'

Caroline racked her brains, then said, 'Oh... Anything by Ibsen.'

'How depressing.' He grimaced. 'Do you like Ibsen?'

'Not really,' she answered honestly, shrugging slim shoulders. 'I like *Hedda Gabler*, but that's about it. Apart from that—he's basically rather grim.'

'I agree,' he said, as though they were two ordinary people having a polite conversation at a cocktail party. 'I prefer passion, drama——'

'Yes, I do too,' she said, relaxing a little. 'I like to feel whirled up and excited by theatre. Dramatic conversations, passionate arguments, hatred and love and desire flooding the stage...'

The grey eyes gleamed at her. 'And Stephen doesn't like that kind of thing?'

'Oh, no,' she said, frowning. 'He's very mild-mannered and easygoing.'

'Have you mentioned your preferences to him?' he asked politely.

'Oh, I couldn't do that,' she said, turning to him. 'He doesn't really know me and I——' she broke off, her face draining of all colour as she stared into his clever, handsome face and saw the trap she had just walked into.

Mark smiled slowly and said, 'Well, well, well.'

Her heartbeat thundered into a gallop. 'I didn't mean it the way it sounded. I——'

'Of course you did,' he said softly, watching her with narrowed eyes. 'You meant every single syllable.'

She coloured hotly. 'You got me to say that, Mark.' Her voice was husky, unsteady. 'You made me think you were talking about plays and——'

'And I wasn't.' He moved towards her, his dark head very close to hers as she shrank back from him. He scrutinised her flushed face with those piercing grey eyes. 'I was talking about your relationship with the man you fully intend to marry. Not much of a relationship, is it?'

'I am going to marry him,' she whispered threadily. 'I am!'

'You can't,' he said deeply, watching her. 'Caroline, you mustn't.'

Her lashes lowered. She found herself staring at the tanned column of his throat and her mouth dried with overpowering desire.

'You're not in love with him,' he said thickly. 'Are you?'

Mute, she raised her green eyes to meet his.

'You've never been in love,' Mark said under his breath. 'Have you?'

Nerveless, she shook her head, staring into his eyes.

'Well, that makes two of us,' he said softly, 'because neither have I. And there's nothing wrong in that, Caroline. Just that you mustn't build marriage on it. Taking mistresses or lovers is one thing. Going up the aisle with them and possibly involving children is quite another.'

'This is none of your business,' she said hoarsely. 'And you're wrong about me. Wrong! I do love Stephen. I——'

'You don't even know the man!' he bit out suddenly, and took her shoulders, pinning her to the couch, eyes blazing. 'More important—he doesn't know you. You just said so yourself!'

'I said he didn't know what kind of plays I liked!' she blustered, shaking in his hands.

'Why don't you want him to know who you really are?' he demanded harshly, hands biting into her slim shoulders as he arched above her. 'Why?'

'He does know me!'

'No! He just knows a beautiful, cool enigma called Caroline Shaw. The same cool enigma who works in my office!'

Her breath caught in shock. 'Enigma...?'

'He's not alone, though, is he?' he said tightly. 'You've been keeping me at a distance for months. Giving me that cool, calm, collected front when underneath you're really a passionate little seductress!'

Her eyes blazed. 'I'm not a passionate little seductress!'

'Not with every man?' he asked under his breath, eyes narrowed.

'No...' she whispered, staring into his eyes.

'Just with me?' he asked thickly.

She tried to get away, a groan coming from the back of her throat.

'That's it, isn't it?' His voice was almost slurred as he stared at her. 'You're really attracted to me. You can't help yourself when I'm near. I bring it all out in you. Don't I, Caro?' He studied her, his grey eyes intense. 'I'm the only man who's ever really seen through you, aren't I?'

White, she couldn't look at him, her heart hammering and her breath strangled in her throat.

'Why do you want to hide from me?' Mark asked thickly. 'Caro, if we made love, you'd be freed. You'd be able to lose yourself in my arms, my darling, and you must be aware of that or you wouldn't be so afraid to——'

'Oh, that's your answer to everything, isn't it, Mark Rider?' she cut in fiercely, lifting her green eyes to meet his with a sudden flash. 'Go to bed and win every prize on the list!'

'It would free you, Caroline,' he said deeply.

'No, Mark. It would make you feel better but it would make me feel like a stupid little tramp!'

His mouth tightened. 'Don't say things like that!'

'What?' she demanded with an angry laugh. 'Stupid? Or tramp?'

'They're neither of them true!'

'They would be if I ever let you make love to me, Mark!'

'Because I'm not prepared to offer you marriage?' he bit out.

'That's right!' she said thickly. 'I won't let you use me, then walk off into the sunset like a conquering hero!'

'I wouldn't do that!' he said forcefully.

'Oh, no?' Her eyes spat contempt. 'How many women have there been, Mark? How many?'

His mouth tightened. He studied her for a second in silence, then said thickly, 'I don't know offhand.'

'Offhand!' she laughed angrily, hatred welling up inside her. 'And you think I'd let a man like you take my body? My virginity? My love? My self-respect?'

He said nothing, watching her in tense silence. She wondered if she'd gone too far, but her principles were screaming at her, as they had from the beginning, not to let Mark win in this battle.

Suddenly, Mark said under his breath, 'What a passionate, emotional woman you are.'

Her eyes closed in swift, appalled self-defence and she could hear her heart drumming as she struggled not to betray the deep fear inside her as she opened her eyes again and met his gaze in the acute silence that followed. When she did meet his intense gaze again, she almost flinched from the depth of recognition in those grey eyes.

'I was right, wasn't I?' he said softly. 'You haven't just been running from me because you want to make love to me. It goes a lot deeper than that.' His hand touched her face. 'You're afraid to reveal yourself to me, aren't you?'

She looked away, said thickly, 'I don't know what you're talking about!'

'If you make love with me,' he said slowly, eyes narrowed, 'you'll show yourself. No more cool controlled Miss Shaw.'

'I never said I was cool and controlled!' she laughed huskily, pulses leaping as she turned her face to look at him through her lashes.

'No,' he said deeply, 'but it is what you want me to believe. And it isn't true, is it? You really are made of fire—not ice.'

She stared into his grey eyes in silence, her mouth dry and her heart thumping.

'I want to get to know you, Caroline,' he said under his breath, 'in every way possible. Beginning with this...'

His mouth closed over hers with a slow sensuality that made her catch her breath with a smothered gasp of pleasure. It was irresistible. She was too excited already, her body leaping with intolerable response, and she could not stop herself opening her mouth beneath his with that swift, hot gasp of delight.

'Mark...' she said against his hard mouth, and her arms moved instinctively to wind around his neck.

He made a harsh sound under his breath and his arms went around her, tightening, his hands pushing up into the silky gold-brown of her long hair and his mouth moved with fiery passion over hers.

Her eyes closed, her head tilted back, she couldn't resist that intoxicating rush of desire like adrenalin to the head, making her dizzy with sensation, a moan coming from the back of her throat.

The kiss deepened without warning, and her heart was slamming harder as she allowed him to slide against her body with his. There was a new feeling in his kiss. He seemed as in need of her touch as she was of his. They wrapped around each other for countless minutes, mouths moving with slow burning hunger, pressing very tightly together.

Mark raised his head, his breathing harsh and rapid. 'Tell me I'm right.' His mouth moved passionately over hers. 'Tell me how I make you feel, Caro. Tell me I see right through you. That I always have.' His voice thickened, his hands were in her silky hair, his lips shaking against her throat. 'Tell me that I make you lose your head, your self-control...that I make that polished mask fragment into a thousand pieces...'

'Yes, yes...' she admitted through swollen lips, her eyes dazed with the force of her passion.

He groaned, and his mouth closed with fierce passion over hers, a harsh sound of excitement coming from the back of his throat as his fingers gripped her harder and she suddenly felt that throbbing pressure of his body communicating his sexual excitement more potently than words ever could.

His heart thudded loudly above her and his strong hands began to move over her body. She gave a hoarse cry of intolerable need, arching against him.

'Oh, God...Caroline!' Mark said hoarsely, and suddenly his hands were shaking as they slid to the zip of her dress. 'I want you more than any woman I've ever known. I've got to make love to you...got to...'

Panic shot through her and she dragged her mouth from his. 'No!' Her face was deeply flushed, green eyes glittering and fevered.

'For God's sake, don't say that again!' he muttered thickly, his heartbeat thudding louder than ever. 'You've just admitted how much you want to make love. How fantastic it would be for both of us. Just let yourself go, Caroline. Don't keep running from me. If we go to bed, I can start to find out who you really are, and I won't reject you, I promise.'

'I don't want to!' she said thickly, a moan in her throat as he licked the pulse that beat there. Her hands tightened in his hair and she whispered, 'Oh, God, Mark...'

'You want me so much you're shaking with it!' he said hoarsely.

Shame burned her cheeks. 'I'm human! I've been locked up in this cottage with you, sleeping with you, looking at you! How can I keep my defences up all the time? They crumble all the time, Mark, because I can't seem to keep them in place when you're around!'

'Caroline!' he said in a shaking voice, his hands moving over her body possessively. 'Oh, God, yes...say that again to me...let me take you upstairs and hear it all night...let me make love to you...'

'What kind of proposition is this, Mark?' she asked shakily, staring into his handsome face. 'Where would it lead if I let you do it?'

'To personal liberty?' he suggested deeply, his hands framing her face.

She gave a bitter laugh. 'Still just sex, then?'

His eyes narrowed. 'It isn't a proposal of marriage, Caroline. It never will be. Haven't I made that clear enough?'

It hurt to hear it, and she felt her mouth tremble as she said huskily, 'Of course! Yes, you've made it very clear. Marriage means a trap to you, Mark, but to me it means love, and that's where we'll never see eye to eye.'

'Darling,' he said under his breath, kissing her, 'see body to body instead. It would be so fantastic...'

'If we were just animals I probably would,' she said, tears pricking the back of her eyes. 'But we're not. We're both people. We have lives to live, and—more importantly—we have ourselves to live with. I'd hate myself if I let you take me.' Her mouth trembled. 'In fact, I'd despise myself. Is that what you really want?'

He gave a harsh sigh. 'Of course it isn't! But I don't see why you'd feel that way, Caro!'

'My body's weak where you're concerned, but my mind isn't.'

'I don't want your mind,' he drawled thickly.

Rage flared in her eyes. 'I'm painfully aware of that! It's precisely why I won't let you take me! Now, just let me go and accept that lovemaking isn't going to happen between us!' Her eyes warred fiercely with his. 'Ever!'

His face ran with dark, angry colour. He stared down at her for a second with angry eyes. 'After everything

I've said? You can still push me away as though I mean nothing to you?'

'Well, what do I mean to you?' she demanded hoarsely. 'Beyond an exciting conquest?'

He looked away, his mouth tightening, and there was a tense silence. Then he said thickly, 'I don't know what you mean to me, Caro. I only know I want you so much I'm going crazy with the need to make love to you.'

She gave a hurt, angry laugh. 'And you have the nerve to lecture me on relationships!'

He looked at her angrily. 'At least I'm not planning to marry someone! At least I'm damned well honest about what I want!'

'Yes!' she said thickly, hating him. 'And I'm honest, too, Mark, when I say I'll never let you make love to me.'

Their eyes warred for a long time. Then he pushed her angrily from him, got to his feet and stared down at her in bitter fury. 'Don't, then, you bloody bitch!' he bit out thickly, towering over her. 'And I shan't ever ask again. Do you get that? Not ever again.'

Hot tears brimmed in her eyes. She felt them slide uncontrollably over her lashes. Mouth trembling, she turned her head, refusing to let him see the agony this intolerable weekend was putting her through. She wanted to give in to him. She wanted it so much that it was killing her. But she didn't dare...

Mark stood over her. 'We're still stuck here together,' he said thickly. 'We have to make the best of it.'

Caroline nodded, face averted as silent tears burned her cheeks.

'We're going to have to eat,' Mark's hard voice commented tightly. 'I'll cook it. What do you want? There are various tins of——' He broke off, studying her averted face. 'Caroline!' he said tightly. 'I'm speaking to you! Kindly look at me!'

She kept her tear-stained face hidden from him. 'I can hear you perfectly well without having to look at you!'

'I said look at me!' he bit out through his teeth.

She did not move and said thickly, 'No!'

It seemed to drive him mad. 'Damn you!' he exploded hoarsely, and his hand shot out to jerk her head back. 'You'll look at me or I'll——' He saw the tears streaming down her face and inhaled sharply as his hand left her head. 'For God's sake, don't cry!' he muttered thickly, and shifted, sighing harshly, running a hand through his hair as she continued to cry in soft sobs. 'Don't cry!' he said again. 'Caroline, don't...'

'I'm so sorry!' she said, tears streaming down her cheeks. 'I'll do my best not to make you feel so uncomfortable in future, but at the moment I really can't help it!'

'Look—I'm sorry,' he said, eyes flickering restlessly over her face. 'I'm not sure what I've done to provoke this, but whatever it is—I'm sorry.'

'What a wonderful apology!' she said rawly, and put her face in her hands, weeping uncontrollably.

He made a rough sound of anger, then sank down beside her, put his arms around her, pressing her wet face into his throat and holding her tightly. 'Come on,' he said thickly. 'Don't cry.'

'It's not your fault,' she said against his strong throat, wet lashes flickering on his tanned skin as she clung to him helplessly. 'You can't help being a selfish, sexist swine!'

He gave a dry laugh, cradling her against him and stroking her hair. 'And you can't help being a woman, I guess. Love, marriage, orange blossom...'

'Do you know how patronising you sound?' she asked huskily, and kissed his throat, grateful for the warmth of his body and his embrace.

'I can imagine,' he said deeply. 'But let's not dwell on it. It's more or less insoluble. Besides—this sudden burst of tears is probably because you're tired and hungry. What say you I carry you into the kitchen and fix you some dinner? A nice glass of red wine. Would that cheer you up?'

She nodded silently, and sniffed like a child.

Mark picked her up, and carried her into the kitchen.

He cooked as he lived, his movements fast, dynamic, efficient and without hesitation. Caroline watched him, her eyes secretly admiring. She loved the way his body moved, loved the lean powerful lines of it, the muscles that rippled beneath the black cashmere sweater and black trousers.

Dinner was chicken and mushroom with instant mashed potatoes and tinned peas. Mark served rich red wine with it, warmed by the stove, and they were both starving, eating hungrily.

Afterwards, they sat replete and warm, finishing the red wine.

'I feel so much better,' Caroline said with a sleepy smile.

He nodded, eyes flickering over her face. 'You look it.'

'Must be the strain, I guess,' she said, and then yawned, her eyes closing completely as weariness overtook her and she gave a long yawning sigh. 'It's so warm in here...!'

'You're exhausted,' Mark said, mouth a firm line, and got to his feet. 'Come on. Bedtime. I'll carry you up, then come back down and do the washing-up, have a glass of wine...'

Caroline smiled sleepily and put her arms around his strong neck. 'By the time you come to bed, I'll be fast asleep.'

'Don't sound too pleased about it,' he drawled with an edge to his voice, and lifted her in his arms, carrying her out of the kitchen and up the stairs.

'I'm not,' she said softly, a haze of wine and his kindness making her impulsively honest. 'I wish this were a different world, Mark. I could let you make love to me, then, and not worry about it.'

He kicked the bedroom door open, looking down at her through hooded lids. 'Would you, Caro?' he asked thickly, putting her down on the bed and watching her intently.

'You know I would,' she said sleepily, and cuddled up to the pillow, a smile on her face as Mark continued to watch her in silence. Her eyes were closing, her ankle throbbing. She needed sleep so badly. When he did not move away, she murmured, 'Aren't you going to light the fire?'

He moved away, and she began to fall asleep as she heard him beginning to build the fire. It had been such a long day, and so emotionally draining. She felt as though she'd been through a whirlwind of passion and desire and excitement...

Mark pulled the duvet up over her with a gentleness she would never have expected from him. He bent his dark head, and kissed her, too, and there was a tenderness in his kiss that made her feel very good indeed.

'Goodnight, Caro,' he said softly, and tiptoed from the room.

CHAPTER TEN

SOME time in the night, Mark slid into bed beside Caroline, his arms moving around her and his body resting against hers. Drowsily, her lids flickered open and she gave a soft sigh, snuggling up to him, breathing in the scent of his body as she rested her face against his strong neck. He tensed momentarily, then held her close, dropping a tender kiss on her head and resting his head against hers.

In the morning, she woke in his embrace.

'Good morning,' he murmured softly, watching her in an odd, enquiring way.

She smiled and snuggled up to him. 'Morning.'

He was silent for a moment, then said idly, 'You talk in your sleep. Did you know that?'

Tensing, she said with a nervous laugh, 'What did I say?'

He stroked her hair. 'I don't really think I should tell you that, Caro.'

She tensed even further, and slowly lifted her head to look up into his strong, handsome, sleepy face. There was a brief silence. He met her gaze with those fascinating grey eyes.

'What did I say?' Caroline asked huskily.

His lashes flickered. 'You said you loved me.'

For a second, she felt as though he'd punched the breath out of her. I didn't say that, her mind informed her. I couldn't have done. I don't feel it, don't even think it. It took every ounce of self-control she had to remain lying there next to him, unmoving, her eyes never once leaving his in that split-second, appalling silence.

Eventually, she said, 'I must have been having a nightmare!'

Mark's hard mouth twisted in a smile. 'I guess so...'

She could scarcely breathe. Her voice said, of its own accord, 'It's the strain, of course.'

Mark's hand slid slowly over her waist. 'We are under a great deal of strain. There's bound to be a severe emotional reaction in us both.'

'And it's not necessarily how we really feel,' she said thickly, grasping in desperation the metaphysical lifeline he was offering.

'Absolutely not,' he said, and his eyes dropped to her mouth.

Excitement gripped the pit of her stomach. Against her thigh, Mark's body hardened with sudden intolerable desire. His heart started to beat very hard and heavily against his chest.

Neither of them moved or spoke. Slowly, Caroline's gaze dropped to his mouth. She swallowed, her mouth intolerably dry. The excitement had flared so suddenly that it was making her blood sing and her temperature rocket out of all control.

Mark slowly lowered his head.

'Don't, Mark...' she whispered with a shiver of excitement.

His mouth closed slowly over hers in a tender kiss, so sensual and undemanding that she gave in at once, her eyes closing and her head tilting back as her hands moved to his dark head and a soft sigh of need came from the back of her throat.

Mark breathed harder, his heart thudded faster, his body pressed hard against her. He slid one strong hand up her slender body until it closed over her breast and felt the fiercely erect nipple. She gave a fierce, involuntary moan of deep satisfaction.

Hunger flared in his kiss like lightning as his mouth explored hers hotly. She was moaning beneath him, utterly lost to his kiss, her mouth open and responsive as her hands moved of their own driven will to his strong neck, his shoulders, and the intolerable need to touch him made her dizzy, insane, wanton.

His breathing was harsh and rapid. 'Let me touch you!' he said thickly against her throat. 'Just let me touch you...' Suddenly, he unzipped her dress and she did not stop him, could not stop him, her heart pulsating as she started to push blindly at his black sweater.

With a hoarse sound, he pulled the sweater from his torso, threw it to the floor, came back to her, kissing her harder. His hands tugged down her dress to the waist.

He drew a ragged breath, lifted his head, looking down into her eyes. Caroline met his penetrating gaze.

Everything seemed to be spinning out of control. She saw his hard-muscled shoulders, bare and tanned, and her breath caught audibly as her gaze moved uncontrollably over his chest, the black hairs curling tightly against that firm muscle-packed flesh.

Dry-mouthed, fingers shaking, she touched him, breathing faster as her hands moved down that powerful chest, encountered his fiercely thudding heart, heard his rough intake of breath and her eyes flashed back with hot desire to meet his.

'Caro...!' he said hoarsely. 'Oh, God...touch me...'

Her shaking hands moved to his taut stomach and he gave a harsh sound of intolerable excitement, bending his dark head, his mouth closing over hers. Desire burst in her like a floodtide. She felt his fingers sliding over her flesh, up over her stomach where her heartbeat made her shake, up to her breasts, and Mark gave a hoarse sound of pleasure as his fingers slid her lacy bra cups down, thumbs stroking her nipples, sending fierce shock-waves of pleasure through her.

Caroline couldn't fight him; her whole body was trembling with the force of her need, she was moving against him slowly, softly, her hands all over his torso, touching him, stroking him, her mouth giving and receiving such intolerable pleasure from his kiss. As he unhooked her bra with shaking hands she started to moan, almost sobbing as he freed her breasts, stroked them, kissing her harder, the pressure of his hardness leaving her in no doubt as to the urgency he too felt.

He raised his head again, breathing raggedly, and watched her face as he slowly, slowly, eased her dress down over her hips.

The dress fell to the floor. He stared down at her, naked as she was but for the silky briefs, her body flushed with heat and pounding with a bloodbeat too powerful to control.

'Oh, God...' Mark whispered, and stared into her eyes with fevered need. 'Caro...Caro...' He lifted her slowly until their naked torsos met and the impact brought a hoarse cry of agonised frustration from Caroline as she ran her fingers down his naked spine.

'Mark...' Her mouth burned against his throat. 'Mark...'

'Let me love you!' he whispered shakily, kissing her hot throat.

'Yes,' she said urgently.

His eyes closed briefly, then he groaned, kissing her, lowering her to the pillows, his body against hers.

'I can't believe you're going to let me make love to you,' he said unsteadily, 'I've waited so long...'

'So have I.' Her mouth seemed swollen, hot, fevered. The frustration and self-denial had never seemed so unbearable. Her hands ran over his naked shoulders in blind desire and she said thickly, 'Take me...take me...'

'Caro...' His lips were shaking as he kissed her hot throat. 'Caro...'

Suddenly, the roar of an engine came from outside.

They both froze, eyes flaring open in horror.

'Not now!' Mark whispered hoarsely.

Voices came from outside too, now, and the lumber of a snow-plough was tempered by the slow crawl of cars.

Mark swore savagely, got off the bed, strode to the window. She watched him, her body trembling with desire. She felt wrenched from paradise.

'We're being rescued,' Mark said harshly, and swung round. 'Get dressed, Caro. They're coming up the path right now.'

Dazed, she was fumbling with her lingerie while Mark dragged on his black sweater. He knelt on the bed behind her, his strong fingers fastening her bra.

'We'll talk on the way back to London,' he said deeply against her throat and kissed her.

Caroline looked round at him. Their eyes met. Her green eyes held deep enquiry, emotion blazing from them as they searched his. He bent his head and kissed her mouth passionately, one hand stroking her neck.

Suddenly, he got off the bed. 'Quickly. Get dressed.'

She got up, began to dress, aware of a smile on Mark's hard mouth as he watched her, a light of some indeterminable kind in his eyes as they flicked over her slender curves.

'Stop watching me,' she murmured, flushing, and he laughed. He insisted on zipping her dress, kissing her when she was dressed.

There was a loud hammering at the front door. Mark swung her into his arms, carrying her downstairs.

'How's your ankle?' he murmured against her hair as they reached the bottom of the stairs.

Surprise lit her eyes as he gently let her stand. 'It doesn't feel anywhere near as painful. I'd forgotten it was sprained, to be honest.'

Outside, they heard the rescue workers shouting at each other.

'They must be in here!'

'Break the door down.'

'Can we do that?'

'Turn the engine off, Bill! We can't hear ourselves think!'

Mark strode to the front door, wrenched it open and an assortment of men in bright plastic work clothes confronted them, a crisp snowy landscape gleaming in bright sunlight behind them.

Suddenly, a tall, handsome blond man stepped forward. 'Is she in there?' he asked hoarsely. 'Is she all right?'

'Stephen...!' Caroline whispered, face draining of all colour, and as Stephen cried her name and ran through the front door Mark stepped back, the grey eyes glittering metallically like silver knives.

She was engulfed in Stephen's arms. 'Darling!' He was kissing her. 'Oh, God, I've been so frantic! I thought you were dead!'

'I'm fine,' she said shakily, staring over his shoulder at Mark's powerful body as he stood talking to a policeman. 'I've hurt my ankle, but not in the crash.'

'Your ankle!' He looked down with concern at her foot.

'Just a sprain.' She was looking at Mark. 'But how did you get here?'

'I saw the news on Sunday night,' Stephen said. 'The whole of Cornwall snowed in. I rang your hotel; they said you hadn't been back since Saturday lunchtime. I drove down late last night, and raised the alarm.'

'I'll write out a cheque for the damage,' Mark was saying coolly to the policeman, and suddenly he turned, striding towards the living-room, and as his grey eyes flicked like steel to meet hers she felt as though she'd been knocked backwards by a nuclear warhead.

I'm in love with him, she thought in a hammerblow of breathless realisation. I've been in love with him all along, from the minute I saw him. That's why I was so wary. I knew I'd fall in love heavily if we ever spent time alone together, and I have...I have...

Pain flooded her...pleasure flooded her. Oh, God, was it possible to feel such extremes of emotion?

'Mark Rider, Ashcroft Manor, Hampshire,' the strong clear voice was saying in the living-room.

'My parents were worried, too,' Stephen was saying. 'I rang and told them before I left, and...'

He continued talking, and she continued staring at him, appalled by the realisation that she would have to break off the engagement. But she couldn't do that now. How could she? He'd just driven all the way from London, organised a rescue team. He might have saved her life. She couldn't possibly tell him here and now that the engagement was over. It would have to wait until he was better able to deal with the news. But meanwhile, she would have to pretend...

'One of our squad cars will take you back to your hotel, sir,' the policeman was saying in the other room. 'And the young lady...?'

'She'll return with her fiancé,' Mark said in a hard voice, and snapped his cheque-book shut.

Pain lanced her heart as she listened. The prick of tears was fierce behind her eyes. Her mouth trembled and she had to swallow hard not to let any tears fall.

Blinking hard, she forced a tight smile for Stephen. 'It was wonderful of you to come,' she said mechanically.

'Darling!' He misinterpreted her blurred vision and pulled her into his arms. 'Oh, my darling, I love you...'

A second later, Mark was striding out of the living-room, his tough face remote and expressionless as he strode past her, shouldering into his black cashmere overcoat, walking out through the open front door, and out of her life...

CHAPTER ELEVEN

THE journey home was akin to returning from Mars in a space shuttle. As Stephen drove across the border from the countryside to the city, she saw the orange street lamps, the neon signs, the skyscrapers and the red-gold smog clinging to the Turneresque sky above London and felt as though she was hurtling through the earth's atmosphere from outer space.

Leaving the cottage had been like burying her own heart. Driving back to the hotel in a squad car had been a test of nerves, because she had known Mark would have checked out, and she was right, but it still hurt to hear the receptionist say it in such a friendly, polite manner. She expected he would have gone to see Jack Rachey on the way home, to get the contract signed. He wasn't the type of man to let personal matters affect business. Then the long drive back to London had begun, and now they were nearly home.

'You must be exhausted,' Caroline said sympathetically to Stephen when they finally pulled up outside the house her flat was in. 'Come in for some coffee and something to eat.'

'Delighted,' groaned Stephen.

'I feel a bit mean asking you to bring my case in,' she said, 'but my ankle . . .'

'I could take you to hospital,' he said at once. 'Perhaps you ought to have X-rays, see if the bone's broken.'

'No, it's getting better already,' she shook her head. 'Besides, Mark felt for a break when it happened, and I trust his judgement.'

'It doesn't hurt any more, then?'

'My ankle is relatively pain-free,' she said huskily, and got out of the car.

The flat seemed strange. Everything was so familiar. Yet everything had changed. Her life had changed during those snowbound days in Cornwall. She was in love for the first time, and the pain that went with her discovery was wrenching. She didn't want to be back here. She wanted to be in the cottage, with Mark, discovering him, falling in love with him, making love...

She cooked Stephen a cheese omelette, served it with salad.

Stephen ate hungrily. 'It must have been awful for you,' he said between mouthfuls, 'stuck in that cottage alone with Mark Rider for a weekend!'

Caroline flicked her gaze from him. 'Yes...' Her voice was husky with pain, yet she felt a sick excitement too, as though something wonderful had happened, something incredible and fantastic, and she wanted to shout it to the whole world, tell everyone her secret. But Mark didn't feel the same. So how would she ever be able to tell anyone? It would have to be a secret forever... and suddenly she no longer wanted to keep secrets. Not from him. Not from Mark.

'Quite appalling.' Stephen shook his head. 'The way he just walked out like that, I mean. He didn't even say goodbye to you, did he? He must dislike you as much as you dislike him.'

She was pale, silent, her face averted.

'What did you do to pass the time?' Stephen asked. 'Or did you just ignore each other?'

'We argued,' she said with a pained smile, and remembered all those arguments with a deep need to return to them, to listen to him talk, watch his handsome face and lean body.

'He really is an arrogant bastard, isn't he?' Stephen drawled, hands behind his head as he leaned back in his chair. 'Everything you told me he was, in fact. Tough, cynical, ruthless. Poor Caroline, getting stuck like that with no one to turn to but him.'

Caroline drew a shaky breath. Was Venetia saying all of this to Mark right now? Jealousy tore through her with such savagery that she could scarcely breathe. How dared he go to another woman, she thought irrationally, how dared he? He's mine...the possessive phrase caused her agony and ecstasy. At last someone who really was hers, all hers, nobody else's. Even if it remained forever a secret, she knew deep inside that Mark was hers. But she could never tell him...

'Never mind, darling.' Stephen was smiling at her. 'It's all over now. You're safe, back home, and with me. We can start making plans. An engagement party, I think. Then there are the wedding arrangements to discuss. My parents want to meet you next weekend...oh, there are a million things to do!'

She looked at him suddenly, shocked by the turn the conversation had taken. Guilt washed over her in waves. I can't leave him like this, she thought. I can't let him talk about a future that is not going to happen.

'Stephen...' she began slowly.

'I know,' he touched her hand. 'You need to rest before we start thinking about——'

'No.' She got to her feet, folding her arms, walking to the window. The London roof-tops seemed to gleam slate grey. 'It's not that, Stephen. I'm afraid it's rather more serious than needing a rest.'

He frowned. 'What do you mean?'

She drew a very deep breath. No point in mincing words. Just be clear and honest and gentle, she thought, and said, 'I mean I can't marry you, Stephen. I'm sorry.'

There was a long silence.

Turning, she saw his stricken face and was consumed with guilt. 'I should never have accepted this ring,' she said unsteadily. 'It was just such a shock, and you'd gone to so much trouble, that I——'

'I can't believe you're saying this!' He spoke hoarsely. 'You were so sure before you went away. You'd agreed to meet my parents, you'd——'

'I did tell you I needed to think about it, Stephen.'

'And over the weekend you did?'

She flushed, nodding.

Stephen looked away. There was a long silence. He raked a hand through his blond hair, his smile angry. Suddenly, he asked, 'What made you change your mind?'

Caroline didn't see the point in hurting him by telling him about Mark. So she said, 'I'm sorry, Stephen. The truth is I just don't feel ready for marriage yet.'

There was another long silence. Then he nodded, unsmiling. 'I can understand that. I mean—obviously, I'm hurt. But at least it's clean cut. It's all above board and honest. After all,' he gave a wry laugh, 'it's not as if there's another man involved!'

Caroline went white, her face pinched.

'I could take anything but that.' Stephen raked a hand through his hair. 'If it was another man—well, I'd go completely berserk. But as the only man you saw since we got engaged was that swine Mark Rider...'

'We can still be friends,' Caroline said huskily, desperate to get off the subject of Mark, 'can't we?'

'Of course.' Stephen got to his feet, his smile pained. 'But I'd rather leave it for a week or two if you don't mind.'

'I quite understand.' Caroline stepped towards him, handed him the engagement ring.

Stephen took it, and stared at it.

Caroline put a hand on his handsome cheek. 'If there's anything I can do...'

'Don't touch me like that!' Stephen winced, brushing her hand away. 'My God, I want to keep my dignity!'

Caroline stepped back at once, eyes filled with sympathy.

'Just keep away from me for the next few weeks,' Stephen said softly. 'Let me get over this alone.' He turned on his heel, strode for the door. 'I'll be in touch...' he said, and left the flat, slamming the door behind him.

When he had gone, she felt overwhelmed by guilt. He had no idea that she had become involved with Mark over the weekend. Nor must he ever suspect. It would only hurt him and make him bitterly angry. And what purpose would it serve? At least I didn't lie to him, she thought: only by omission, and then to save his feelings and his pride.

Liz came in at six.

'Wow!' she laughed as she saw Caroline in the living-room. 'The abominable snowman returns!'

Caroline looked up, green eyes pain-filled. 'Hi...'

Liz dropped her keys on the sofa, moving towards her at once. 'Caro, what on earth is it? You look absolutely devastated.'

Caroline held out her naked left hand.

Liz stared. 'Oh, no! The engagement's off? But why? What happened?'

'Mark Rider happened,' she said with hoarse bitterness, and her hands flew to her face. 'Oh, my God, Liz! I fell in love with him. I fell in love...'

'What?' Liz sank down beside her on the chair arm, eyes filled with concern. 'Caro...'

'He took me away for the weekend to seduce me,' Caroline said thickly, the need to tell someone suddenly overwhelming. 'I refused, of course, so he offered to make me his mistress. Luxury apartment, fast car, charge account at Harrods—you know the kind of thing.'

'What a heel!'

'I refused that, too.' Caroline laughed, tears stinging the back of her eyes. 'Then we crashed in the blizzard and got trapped in a cottage together for forty-eight hours. It was hellish, Liz. I'm so attracted to him...I couldn't stop him every time he tried to seduce me.'

'Couldn't stop him...' Liz repeated in horror.

Hot colour flooded her face. 'I didn't give in to him, don't worry about that. But the more I didn't, the more he tried. It was just a remorseless seduction. The whole weekend.'

'He's a very sexy man,' Liz agreed with a sigh. 'I can't think how you resisted.'

'It was so difficult,' she whispered. 'We had to sleep together to keep warm. We had to eat together, talk to each other, wake up together, share a bathroom, a kitchen, swap confidences...'

'Like living with him,' Liz said, nodding slowly. 'Yes, I can see exactly what happened. You relaxed with a man completely for the first time in your life, and the result was that you fell in love.'

She caught her breath, staring, then said in a husky rush, 'But, Liz, I don't see how it happened or——'

'That's the point though, lovey,' Liz said, smiling. 'You *don't* see. It's not like getting a job. It's an invisible process that builds up slowly and naturally, and suddenly hits you when you least expect it.'

She stared, pulses leaping. 'But I—I feel so emotional and——'

'Well, you would.' Liz laughed, grey eyes gentle. 'Caro, you've been sealed off all your life from real relationships. I've lived with you for a year now, and this is the first time we've *ever* had a conversation like this.'

Caroline flushed. 'I'm so rarely at home and——'

'No,' Liz said quietly. 'You just automatically behave as though you have no feelings or personal life or even a need to confide.'

'But how could I have fallen in love with Mark in just two days?' she asked hoarsely. 'Even if I was forced to— have a real relationship with him?'

'Because he was the right guy,' Liz said, smiling. 'It was obviously fate that threw you together in that snowbound cottage.'

'If only that were true!' Pain struck her heart and she said bitterly, 'But it's not. He's not in love with me, Liz.'

'Isn't he? You surprise me. From the sound of him, he's a similar creature. Otherwise, why would he have mistresses?'

'Because he's an attractive swine,' she said bitterly. 'A sexy, arrogant bastard. You can string all the adjectives you like together in a variety of ways, but they still describe Mark's attitude to women.'

Her frown deepened. 'You mean there was no change in his attitude towards you? Through the whole course of the weekend? Oh, I can't believe that, Caro!'

'Why not?' she asked huskily. 'You know what kind of man he is!'

'Yes, but this can't be a one-way thing.' Liz said, 'Not in these circumstances. When a relationship deepens to this extent, it's always a shared experience.'

Later that night, Caroline lay in bed staring at the dark, sifting through her shell-shocked mind to try to find some grain of hope in Liz's words.

Mark's attitude towards her *had* changed over the weekend. That had been obvious when he'd very nearly made love to her before the rescue people arrived. But that must have been the need to satisfy his lust. He'd waited long enough, after all, and most men in his situation would probably have been shaking with lust by the time the woman gave in.

Bitter tears scalded her cheeks as she remembered how Mark had strode out of the cottage without a word, without so much as a backward glance. So much for talking on the way back to London!

No doubt his tenderness towards her in the bedroom had been born of a desire to keep her ready to make love to him once they returned to London. But when Stephen arrived, he'd realised his opportunity was lost forever.

Tomorrow she would have to face Mark at the office, and what would she say? How would she act? The thought of it was terrifying, but she steeled herself to do it.

One thing was clear, though. She must not tell him her engagement to Stephen was over. If he knew that, he would realise he could renew his pursuit and eventually persuade her into bed with him. They both knew now that she wouldn't be able to resist him if he was persistent enough, but the thought of making love to him, knowing she loved him so deeply and was un-loved in return, filled her with deep horror.

In fact, it made her cry herself to sleep in silent misery...

Next day, she arrived at the office exactly on time. Shaking with nerves, she hung up her coat as usual, and moved towards the desk, her heart pounding loudly.

The buzzer on the intercom went loudly. Her pulses jumped like crazy. She took a deep breath, leaned over and depressed the key.

'Yes, sir?' Her voice was as steady as she could make it.

'Bring in the mail, Miss Shaw.' Mark's voice was strong and clear and her heart sank as she realised how completely he felt nothing for her but lust.

'Right away.' She felt like crying, but was far too proud. She picked up the stack of mail, lifted her head, and walked the few feet to his office door.

Her heart almost burst at the sight of him, leaning back in his chair, hands clasped behind his arrogant dark head. He wore a stylish grey suit, a silk tie, a tight waistcoat, a gold watch chain. He looked unbearably gorgeous. She wanted to kiss his handsome mouth, run her fingers through his black hair, feel his strong hands on her body...

Their eyes met and she felt as though she was falling down a mine shaft, her heart plummeting with love. Mark looked away and her heart dropped on to a knife.

'Good morning, sir,' she said in a clipped, professional voice and walked to the desk in her high heels and red silk shift dress.

'Good morning,' he said tightly, and his eyes flashed over her body. 'You got home all right, then?'

'Stephen drove me,' she said, and handed him the mail.

'Ah, yes!' he drawled unpleasantly. 'The plastics man and his——' He broke off with an indrawn breath as his eyes shot to her left hand, then to her face.

Flushing, Caroline stepped away from him, horror in her eyes as she tried to drag that betraying left hand behind her back.

'It's over,' Mark said thickly, and his hand shot to her left wrist, jerking her towards him as he studied her bare hand. 'Who broke it off, Caro? You or him?'

'None of your business!' she said shakily, furious with herself for not realising he would notice at once that her ring was gone.

'None of my business!' he bit out, getting to his feet. 'What the hell are you talking about?'

'My personal life,' she said unsteadily, struggling to get away from him. 'It is and always will be none of your business!'

He towered over her, silver eyes leaping with fury. 'Don't tell me it had nothing to do with me, because I won't believe it. It was all you talked about in that damned cottage. Your wonderful, rosy marriage to Stephen Daly complete with bluebirds flying around your entwined heads!'

'Shut up, you cynical——'

'What happened, Caro?' he demanded. 'Did you tell him what happened between us there?'

Hot colour flooded her face. 'Nothing happened between us!' she said unsteadily, avoiding his eyes. 'Nothing...'

His hands gripped her shoulders, dragging her towards his hard body. 'Now look me in the face and say that!' he said under his breath.

Caroline closed her eyes, her head jerking away from him.

'I said look me in the face, you little bitch!' he bit out under his breath, and his fingers clamped like a steel vice on her flushed face as he turned it ruthlessly to his.

Her eyes opened. She stared into the glittering silver eyes. 'Nothing happened between us...' she whispered, heart banging.

'You practically went to bed with me. You offered yourself to me. If those damned rescue workers hadn't come along, I'd have had you, and then where would you be—looking me in the eye and telling me nothing happened?'

Furious, she struggled against him, breaking away, backing, her body shaking and her eyes blazing fierce green. 'Just sex! That's all! You nearly seduced me—so what? It didn't happen, and now that we're out of that claustrophobic situation it never will!'

He stared, his fists clenching at his sides, breathing hard. Suddenly he said in a tight voice, 'Who broke off the engagement, Caro?'

She blinked rapidly, too shocked at the sudden change of attack to speak.

His eyes were intent on her face. 'Was it you?'

She flinched, turned her back on him. She couldn't lie. Not directly. But she couldn't tell him it had been her decision. It would reveal her true feelings for Mark, and she couldn't let him see them.

'Answer me, you obstinate——!' he swore savagely. 'Answer me!'

'No,' she said, tight-lipped, trembling.

He bit out an expletive under his breath and slammed a hand violently on the desk.

'Temper tantrums, Mark?' Caroline said thickly, turning, seeing him standing with violent brooding fury. 'They won't do you any good. You can shout and bully as much as you like, but it won't make me reveal a shred of my personal life to you.'

His eyes were a violent grey. 'Nothing's changed, then? You're still the same frigid, close-mouthed little——'

'I'm still my own person,' she clipped out through pale lips. 'And the only power you have over me is during working hours.'

His face grew black with rage. 'I see. That's the way we're going to play it. Very well, then, Miss Shaw,' he bit out. 'Get into your office, and get me Venetia Blake on line one. The private line, if you recall.'

Jealousy flared in her with such savagery that she could only stare at him, green eyes livid, mouth rigid, body trembling with the force of her raging emotions.

Mark laughed cruelly under his breath. 'Oh, you can dish it out but you sure as hell can't take it.'

Her face flamed. 'I don't know what you're talking——'

'Get in your office, Miss Shaw, and do as you're told,' he bit out. 'And while you're at it, I want Jack Rachey on line two in three minutes. He's in London, at the

Ritz, and you and I will be lunching with him there at one o'clock.'

Caroline struggled to control herself, lifting her head with savage dignity and giving a brief, curt nod. Turning on her heel, she left the office and closed the door with a harsh click behind her.

She started to shake at once. Stumbling to her desk, she had to lean on it for a split second, breathing in shallow breaths. Then she pulled herself together and picked up the phone, ringing Venetia Blake, though it killed her to have to do it.

'Just putting you through, Miss Blake,' she said, and pressed the button for Mark's private line.

He answered at once. 'Venetia,' his deep, smoky voice was seduction itself. 'Darling, I've missed you...'

Caroline hung up with a crash, jealousy blazing savagely in her veins. Damn him! Damn her! Damn them both!

She worked steadily through the morning, typing up the letters Mark had already dictated before she arrived. Listening to his strong, cool voice in her ears made her pulses race, memories of his lovemaking exploding in her mind, heart and body.

At half-past twelve, the door opened and Mark strode out, dynamic, powerful, handsome and impeccably dressed.

'Ready, Miss Shaw?' he drawled, eyes like knives. 'Lunch with Rachey at the Ritz, remember?'

Caroline got to her feet tensely, the red silk shift dress she wore rippling as she walked, highlighting her slender hourglass figure, and Mark's eyes lingered on her full breasts as she approached him.

'I should have taken you and left the rescue workers to break the door down,' he drawled cynically. 'I'd feel so much better if I'd had you in every possible sense of the word.'

She sucked in her breath sharply and said, 'If you make one more remark like that, I'll resign, you bastard!'

He laughed softly. 'Just get your coat, Miss Shaw...'

They were driven to the Ritz by Mark's chauffeur, and the Rolls-Royce limousine was luxurious, but the electricity flashing between her and her boss was intolerable. Her eyes kept lingering on his tough profile. She was aware of his narrowed gaze on her body. She kept wanting him to push her backwards and kiss her till her legs gave way...

The Ritz was crowded. Waiters swished about in black tails. The Palm Court glittered under the glass dome, sunlight pouring over marble and gold and green palms.

Mark strode ahead of her with customary dynamism, up the marble steps, hands thrust in Savile Row trouser pockets, every woman in the place eyeing him with breathless admiration.

'Mr Rider, sir!' The head waiter bowed. 'Wonderful to see you. I have your favourite table ready...'

They were lead across to a long pink-gold couch and long marble table. 'Ritz Cuvée champagne,' Mark ordered coolly, sinking down with predatory masculine grace on the couch as Caroline sank down beside him, heart thudding with savage love for him.

'Rachey appears to be late,' she said, dry-mouthed, when he looked at her with those fantastic grey eyes.

'True to form,' he said curtly, gaze flicking to her mouth. 'I expect he's still in his room and——'

'Mark!' A voice drawled, making them both look round. A tall dark man stood at their table, smiling at them both in a nasty way. 'But how interesting to see you! May I ask who the young lady is?'

Mark's eyes narrowed. 'My secretary, Miss Shaw.' He glanced at her, saying slowly, 'Caroline, this is Paul Devonshire, the gossip columnist of the *Daily Gazette*.'

Caroline's eyes widened with recognition. 'How do you do?' She extended a pale, slim hand.

Paul Devonshire shook hands with her, smiling. 'Just the secretary, eh? A pity. I thought you might be Mark's latest. I'm here to pick up useful titbits, you see, because there's not much going on in the——'

'I can assure you she is only my secretary,' Mark cut in icily. 'And we're here for a business lunch with Jack Rachey, one of our oldest clients. Now, if you'll excuse us, we have some business to discuss.'

There was a little silence, then Paul Devonshire smiled. 'OK. Perhaps another time, then?' Turning, he strolled in his expensive suit back to his table.

As he sank down, Caroline's eyes flickered past him, and she froze with horror, staring at Stephen Daly, a few tables behind Devonshire, staring with a fierce gaze of terrible misery straight at her.

'Oh, my God...' she whispered, tensing.

Mark shot her a narrow-eyed look. 'I agree, Devonshire is a nuisance, but he's got nothing on either of us, so you can relax.'

She moistened her lips, glanced at him, and decided to say nothing about Stephen's presence here at the Ritz. He must have come here to reminisce on the evening he'd asked her to marry him. How long ago that seemed! Should she go over and speak to him? She remembered

him telling her to keep away from him. She picked up
her champagne glass and drank. Better abide by his
wishes and not approach him.

'You're very pale,' Mark said tightly beside her. 'I'm
sure the thought of being reported in the *Gazette* as my
latest mistress is quite abhorrent to you.'

She flushed, put down her glass. 'That's right.'

'But it was so nearly true, wasn't it?' he drawled unpleasantly. 'How well I remember those moments on the
bed. The way you——'

'Shut up,' she said under her breath, face tight.

'That's not quite what you said, is it? Let me see
now...' He leaned closer, eyes narrowed, and whispered
thickly in her ear, '"Mark, take me! Make love to me...I
want you to..."'

Hot colour flooded her face. Her pulses were leaping
violently. 'If you don't stop this, Mark, I shall resign
and——'

'You resign, missy,' he bit out under his breath, 'and
I'll be at your flat in five seconds flat to take what you
so passionately offered me at the cottage!'

'You wouldn't get it offered to you a second time,'
she said through tight lips.

'Want to bet on that?' he said through his teeth.

Their eyes met and warred. Caroline's body was
jumping with hot desire, love running like wildfire
through her heart, and she suddenly knew she had to
get away from him to think.

'I'll go up to Rachey's room and get him,' she said
thickly, and got to her feet. 'I shan't be long...'

Before he could stop her, she was on her feet and
walking across the Palm Court, her legs weak beneath
her. She had to resign. There was no question now. Even

if he carried out that threat, she knew she wouldn't let him take her, however deep the temptation.

Walking into the shelter of the lift alcove, she leant weakly against the wall, hidden from view by the archway, breathing in shallow gasps as she thought of her future. In love with Mark, leaving the firm, her engagement over, going into the future with nothing... nothing...

Mark strode into the lift alcove suddenly, face black with rage. 'Don't you ever walk out on me in the middle of a sentence like that again!'

She stared at him, feeling weak with love. 'Jack Rachey is fifteen minutes late! I didn't want to just sit there and wait for him when we all know he could be——'

'You didn't walk out because of that!' he bit out. 'You walked out because what I was saying was unacceptable to you! Do you think I'm stupid?'

Her face flamed. 'Well, what do you expect? You were reminding me of my own folly at the cottage and——'

'It wasn't folly,' he said thickly, towering over her with an air of menace. 'It was natural. You wanted me, you've always wanted me, you still want me and you——'

'Why are you doing this?' she whispered shakingly. 'You know it's impossible, you know it's over——'

'It'll never be over until I make love to you!' he cut in harshly.

There was a breathless silence. She stared into his eyes.

'Mark, don't...' she whispered, legs going weak.

'I've tried to stop it,' he said under his breath. 'Tried to play boss to your secretary all bloody morning, but I just can't forget the woman you are, Caro.'

'You only want me in your bed...'

'And how!' he said thickly, and his hands slid onto her shoulders.

Her pulses leapt violently. 'Oh, God...don't touch me!'

Fury blazed in his eyes. 'The hell I won't!' he said hoarsely, and then he was dragging her against his hard body, his mouth closing over hers with ruthless hot insistence.

Excitement leapt in her veins. Moaning in hoarse need, she opened her mouth to his fiery kiss, and heard his rough gasp of desire as he pressed her against the wall, his hard thighs against hers and his hands moving over her body while she shook, whispering his name, pushing her hands shakingly through his black hair.

A footfall behind them made them break apart wildly, flushed and fevered.

Stephen stood in the doorway, white, shell-shocked, devastated.

'Oh, no...' Caroline's shaking hands went to her bruised mouth. 'Stephen...'

Stephen stepped forwards angrily. 'This is the real reason you broke off our engagement, isn't it? Him! That swine you profess to hate so much! But you don't hate him, do you? You bloody well fancy him! You're in love with him! You're——'

'Stephen, you're misinterpreting——' she began in agony.

'You went to bed with him over the weekend!' Stephen said fiercely. 'You're his mistress! You're——'

'Shut up!' Mark bit out, taking a violent step towards him as Paul Devonshire strolled innocently into the archway, then stopped dead, his gaze flashing from face to face as he froze where he stood and a gleam entered his eyes.

'I will not shut up!' Stephen was saying furiously, unaware of Devonshire standing right behind him. 'I was engaged to Caroline before you took her away for the weekend. You seduced her, didn't you? You made her your mistress and ruined my life and now——'

'I didn't make her my mistress.' Mark lifted his dark head, a ring of hard authority in his voice as he put his arm around Caroline. 'But I fully intend to make her my wife.'

CHAPTER TWELVE

'How could you have said that?' Caroline demanded hoarsely as the chauffeur-driven Rolls sped back across West London. 'Poor Stephen was so hurt. He just walked away with a face like stone, and I had to let him go because that awful man was listening——'

'It was precisely because Devonshire was listening that I said it,' he bit out. 'How many more times have I got to tell you?'

'I could have lived it down,' she said, running a hand through her gold-brown hair. 'Even if he'd printed the story, I would have survived it. Not everyone reads the *Gazette*. And not everyone believes what they read in the papers, anyway.'

'Fine,' he said tightly beside her in the luxurious rear of the limousine. 'But I wasn't letting Daly get away with any of that, either.'

She winced at the memory. 'Poor Stephen. I shall have to go and see him, talk to him, make him understand . . .'

'You'll do no such thing,' he said tightly, eyes warring with hers.

'Mark, I must try to make amends.'

'You can't,' he said flatly. 'Leave him alone to get over it in his own time, Caro. Any contact from you will only make it harder for him.'

She gave a miserable sigh. 'I suppose you're right . . .'

'Besides,' his voice was tough, 'he can't have been in love with you, or he would never have said all of that. He knows perfectly well you wouldn't have slept with

173

me. Unless . . .' His grey eyes darted over her face and his face drained slowly of all colour.

Caroline looked up, meeting his gaze, and caught her breath at the expression there.

'Unless you've been to bed with Daly,' Mark said through white lips.

She just stared at him, thinking, Does he care?

'Well?' he bit out thickly, his hand catching her chin. 'Answer me, Caro, or so help me I'll strangle you with my bare hands!'

'What do you want to know?' she asked, heart leaping violently.

He was silent for a long moment, then his deep voice asked unsteadily, 'Have you let Daly make love to you?'

She considered telling him it was none of his business. Then she wondered with tears in her eyes what would be the point. Lowering her lashes to hide her tears, she whispered, 'No, Mark. No, I haven't let Stephen make love to me.'

He expelled his breath harshly, his hand still on her chin. His grey eyes watched her bent head. The car sped through London, slowing for a set of traffic lights.

Mark released her slowly, then murmured, 'We'll have to get you a ring.'

Her lashes flickered wetly and she looked up, tensing. 'A ring?'

'An engagement ring,' he said flatly and leant forwards, rapping on the glass. 'Take us to Cartier's!'

Caroline caught her breath, whitening, grabbing his powerful forearm. 'Mark, for God's sake, you can't be serious!'

He looked down at her, black brows jerking together. 'Of course I'm serious! Caro—I told the most famous gossip columnist in England that I intended to marry you! I'm not backing down!' He sat back, his eyes a harsh grey. 'I'm marrying you, whether you like it or not.'

'But...' Her lips were bleached. 'But...you can't mean it! We can't marry. We're not in love, we——'

'Shut up,' he said bitingly, his face hard. 'Love is bloody irrelevant.'

Pain shot through her. 'It may be to you, but it's not to me!'

'You're hardly qualified to lecture on the subject!' he bit out thickly. 'You broke that engagement to Daly, you broke his heart and you accepted his proposal without loving him enough to follow it through!'

She sucked in her breath, whitening. 'My God, you swine!'

He gave a harsh laugh. 'That's rich! All I did was try to get you into bed. At least I didn't go all out to smash your heart into tiny pieces!'

She jerked her face away before he could see the broken pieces of her heart in her green eyes.

'Why did you break the engagement, Caro?'

'I...' Her heart was banging violently. 'I just realised I couldn't marry him. That's all.'

He watched her in silence, then asked unsteadily, 'Anything to do with me? I mean—what happened between us?'

Caroline shook her head but could not speak.

The Rolls stopped outside Cartier's. He glanced up at it, then at her bent head. 'Daly said something about your being in love with me.'

She froze, not daring to look round, her pulses leaping violently.

Mark waited, then said, 'Just jealousy, I guess? No truth in it.'

She swallowed, her throat dry, then said huskily, 'No truth in it.'

He was very still suddenly and the silence lengthened until she turned her head slowly to look up into his tough face. At once, he looked away, his hand reaching for the door-handle.

'Let's get that ring,' he said thickly, and stepped out of the car.

Caroline stepped out, green eyes a fire in her white face as she watched him stride round to her, his body arrogant and his face hard.

'Mark,' she touched his arm as they stood outside that fabled black-gold window, 'I can't do it.'

He stared down at her, mouth tight. 'I've announced it. There's no way back for either of us.'

Pain lit her eyes. 'But marriage, Mark! I know how you feel about it! You'll hate me for trapping you, we'll fight all the time, we'll——'

'You'll marry me if I have to drag you to the altar by your long hair, Caro!' he bit out thickly, and dragged her into Cartier's with hard possessive fingers.

They looked at rings in a silence fraught with tension. The jewels blazed on black velvet and she stared down at them in an agony of emotion, thinking, I've fallen in love with him and now I'm going to have to pay for it in blood during a marriage that will be a battlefield of love and hate.

'The ruby,' she said hoarsely, seeing it suddenly blazing in silver against that black velvet, the silver of his eyes.

Mark reached for it wordlessly, then his eyes flicked slowly to meet hers. They studied one another in silence. His hand found hers, slid the ring on to her finger, the cool metal a brand on her skin.

Mark turned to the jeweller. 'We'll take it,' he said thickly. 'Send me the box it comes in and the bill. My fiancée will wear it as we leave.'

'Very good, Mr Rider,' murmured the jeweller with a discreet nod.

They left in silence, got into the rear of the Rolls. Caroline was trembling, staring down at the ruby on her finger, and she looked ravishing, her red silk dress a blaze against the white of her skin and the long silky gold-brown of her hair.

Mark said thickly, 'We can't go back to the office.'

Wordlessly, she looked up at him.

'We'll just be inundated with calls,' he said, staring at her through those hooded eyelids. 'I think we should take the rest of the day off and go back to my place.'

Her eyes widened. 'Mark, we can't! Jack Rachey's signature is on that contract now and——'

'And it can wait till tomorrow,' he said flatly, and rapped on the glass partition. 'Ashworth Manor, and make it snappy!'

Her heart leapt. She was finally going to see his home. 'We're going to Hampshire?'

'It seems sensible,' he said, looking away from her. 'If we're going to be married, you'll have to see where I live and——'

'I'm still far from sure we should even be considering marriage!' she said thickly. 'We don't even get on, let alone love each other.'

His face tightened. 'Just shut up and accept it, Caro!'

She closed her eyes and looked out of the window in silent misery for the rest of the journey. The car sped out of London, through green fields, eventually turning off the motorway and sliding along narrow country lanes until they sped through the gates of Ashworth Manor.

It was a beautiful house, a red-brick Elizabethan manor set in acres of sweeping parkland, deer grazing by a lake, a few acres of forest to the west, and the house itself twisting in Tudor beauty against a halcyon blue sky.

They stepped out on to a gravel drive and Mark said flatly, 'I'll give you a quick tour of the main rooms. There's too much to see all at once.'

Caroline met his gaze bitterly. 'I feel like an employee.'

His grey eyes blazed. 'Well, you're not!' he bit out thickly and took her wrist in hard fingers. 'You're my fiancée—remember? You're wearing my bloody ring and we're going to be married; now stop trying to get out of it!'

He pulled her angrily behind him as they went up the steps and through the vast arched doorway.

'Sir!' The butler did a double-take as he saw Mark enter with Caroline. 'I had no idea you'd be home so soon. Did you telephone or——?'

'No, Bellamy,' Mark said flatly, striding past him. 'And if there are any calls for me, I'm not here. Is that clear?'

'Yes, sir.' Bellamy watched curiously as Mark strode to the staircase, his hand around Caroline's wrist, dragging her after him up the sweeping staircase. 'Very good, sir.'

They were on the long wood-panelled landing suddenly, and Caroline said with hoarse fury, 'You're taking me straight to the bedrooms, are you? I might have known it! You've made it clear all along that——'

'I want to speak to you privately,' he said tightly, and pushed open a bedroom door, thrusting her inside forcefully. 'What's more private than a bedroom?'

Caroline backed from him, her heart hammering violently, the double four-poster bed rising behind her and making her panic. 'No one would disturb us if we were downstairs! You just want——'

'To ask you a few questions,' he said thickly, and locked the door.

She stared through her lashes, her legs weak beneath her, so weak that she thought she might fall.

Mark watched her across the room. 'Why did you break off your engagement to Stephen Daly?'

She swallowed. 'That's none of your——'

'Don't say it,' he said huskily, and walked slowly towards her, standing in front of her, looking down at her face with intense grey eyes. 'Don't tell me it's none of my business, Caro,' he said deeply. 'In fact—don't ever say that to me again. Ever.'

'Why?' she asked hoarsely, green eyes bitter. 'Because you've forced us both into a marriage we don't want?'

His face tightened. 'I thought you wanted marriage above and beyond anything else on earth?'

She flushed hotly, lowering her lashes. 'I did.'

'So what happened to change your mind?'

She couldn't possibly answer that.

He slid a hand under her chin, forced it upwards, the grey eyes narrowed. 'What happened in that cottage, Caroline?' he asked under his breath. 'And don't say I know what happened, because I don't. I was there, but I can't read your mind...' his lashes flickered '...or your heart.'

Caroline tried to get away, panic erupting in her.

'No!' he said thickly, holding on to her. 'You don't get away. That's why I brought you up here. Trapping you behind a locked door is the only way to make you speak to me.'

'Don't, Mark!' she whispered, her shaking hands moving for support to his broad shoulders. 'I don't want to talk about it.'

'Why did you change your mind about marriage?' Mark asked, remorseless as always. 'Why? You wanted nothing but marriage. *Now*, it's the last word in unreasonable behaviour.'

'Marriage to you!' she said fiercely. 'That's all I object to!'

'Your memory is failing,' he said thickly. 'You just broke your previous engagement—after a weekend snowbound with me. Don't tell me there's no connection, because I don't believe it.'

Colour flooded her face. Suddenly, she couldn't stand it any longer, and her heart thudded fit to burst as she stared bitterly into his face and shook with the force of her emotions.

'I don't want to talk about it!' she shouted hoarsely. 'Can't you get that through your thick head?'

He looked at her in rigid, violent silence, his face dark red.

Caroline gave a hoarse sob, and broke away from him.

He caught her wrist and said thickly, 'Caroline, I'm in love with you.'

Her heart stopped beating. The silence was acute. She had to struggle to breathe. Slowly, she looked round at him, but his face was averted, his hand like iron on her wrist as he looked away from her.

Trembling, she said hoarsely, 'What did you say?'

His eyes closed and his mouth tightened. 'I said I'm in love with you. I fell in love with you. You've changed my life. I want to marry you.' He gave a harsh laugh, looking at her, his grey eyes filled with bitter, savage emotion. 'How many different ways do you want it? It still amounts to the same thing!'

She hesitated, her heart pounding fit to burst, then gave a hoarse cry of love and flew at him, her arms around his neck as she whispered, 'Mark . . . I fell in love with you, too!'

'Do you mean it?' he whispered thickly, his arms going around her and holding her tightly.

She was raining kisses on his face and throat. 'Yes, yes, my darling! I couldn't bear it when you just walked out like that without saying goodbye. It was like having a limb amputated. I wanted to die . . .'

'You went into Daly's arms and burst into tears,' he said deeply, burying his face in her throat. 'I felt crucified. I wanted to smash him in the face, drag you away shouting, "She's mine, get your bloody hands off her!"'

'I had to let him down gently,' she whispered fiercely. 'He'd driven all that way, gone to so much trouble...how could I just tell him point-blank that I wasn't going to marry him?'

'When did you know?' he asked, raising his dark head to look down at her with those fierce eyes. 'When did you know you were in love with me?'

'When they broke into our world,' she whispered, stroking his dark hair. 'It was such an intrusion, so shattering to our personal world...I wanted to slam the door and stay in that cottage with you forever.'

His hard mouth curved in a smile. 'Yes . . . I felt that. It was the same moment for me. I had no idea what was happening until then. But all the time, all weekend, I was being forced to see you as another person, not just a woman I wanted to make love to, but more than that— a woman with feelings and a history and thoughts and dreams and ambitions: you were so real to me, and the more time I spent with you, the more I could feel it happening... discovery... falling in love...'

'You didn't show it,' she whispered, staring. 'I was convinced you hated me more and more as the weekend went on.'

'I was shaken by it all,' he said deeply, stroking her face with tender fingers. 'It was such an unstoppable process. I resented it, fought it, struggled against it. Then suddenly they broke into our world and I no longer had any choice; it was over. We were both going back to London, to the office, to a relationship that was so impersonal I wanted to shout and smash things at the thought of it.' He kissed her face. 'My darling, I couldn't bear it. I liked waking up beside you. I liked watching you cook for me, I liked looking after you when your ankle went, I liked talking to you at the drop of a hat...'

She smiled tremulously. 'Yes... I liked it, too. I even liked your bad temper and your endless attempts to seduce me.'

He laughed, drawling, 'I'm pleased to hear it! I can't believe you could be in love with me if you didn't like my touch.'

Her eyes fell to his mouth. 'Oh, I like your touch,' she whispered, her heart beating much too fast. 'I like it... very, very much.'

His breath caught sharply, and his eyes darkened. 'Don't tempt me, Caroline,' he said in an unsteady voice. 'I'll want to make love to you, and I mustn't do that. Not if you're to love me as I need you to.'

She frowned, disappointed so deeply it was impossible to speak.

'Darling,' Mark said huskily, 'I want this to be a real marriage. I want to be able to wake up beside you for the rest of my life. I want you to cook for me, talk to me, argue with me, throw things at me, slap my face when I go too far and slam doors at the end of a row.' His grey eyes held teasing laughter. 'If you believe I only married you to get you to bed—how will you be able to love me that much?'

'You... you mean you don't want to make love to me any more?' she said in hoarse agony, staring into his grey eyes, the prospect of it appalling to her. 'Mark...for God's sake, don't say that! I want to love all of you. I keep thinking about it, and I understand it now, I can see that making love is just that. It's the closest I can get to your soul. To give you physical pleasure will make my head spin. It's not just that I want you to make love to me.' Her heart thudded wildly. 'Mark... *I* want to make love to *you*.'

He stared down at her, his hands tightening on her waist, and said nothing, but she heard and felt his heart begin to beat thuddingly against his chest, and her eyes slowly moved to it, encountering the strong column of his tanned throat, and suddenly desire flashed through her like fire.

Breathing unsteadily, she lifted trembling hands to his throat and began to loosen his tie.

Mark was rigid, breathing thickly, staring as she slid that silk tie off with a swish and let it fall to the floor, her eyes darting back to his as she shakingly began to unbutton his shirt, exposing his hard-muscled chest, the black hairs that curled there, the heartbeat that thudded so hard beneath skin and bone.

Dry-mouthed, she bent her head, her mouth moving seductively over his chest.

'Oh, God...!' Mark bit out thickly, and suddenly he was pulling her face up to his, his mouth crushing hers, and they kissed like one person, desperate to get so close to the other that their souls merged along with their bodies.

He lifted her in his arms, carrying her to the bed.

'Are you sure about this?' he whispered hoarsely as he lay down beside her, breathing harshly. 'My darling, I'm prepared to wait. It's not vital to me to make love to you now. I want you like hell, but I want your love far more.'

'Take both,' she whispered, her fingers stroking his bare chest, and then she started to push his shirt and jacket back off his broad, muscled shoulders.

He shouldered out of them, his face dark red with desire, and threw them to the floor. He came back to her, and his mouth covered hers with a deep, demanding kiss that shook her to her roots. She moaned, running her hands over his chest and spine and shoulders and stomach, revelling in his harsh gasps of pleasure. His hands unzipped her dress, tugged it down to the waist, covered her breasts, unleashed them from the lacy bra, stroking them as she gave long shaking moans of pleasure as his fingers stimulated her erect nipples.

'Love me . . .' she said thickly, clutching his dark head as they kissed. 'Love . . .'

Mark's heart slammed violently and he tugged her dress off completely, sliding between her slender thighs, his hair-roughened chest clamping against her as his hands unhooked the lacy bra she wore, and dropped it to the floor, rubbing her breasts as she stroked his chest, bending his dark head to suck her nipples and feel the wild slam of her heartbeat.

He shed his clothes with urgency, coming back to her naked, and she moaned in delirium at the sight of him, her hands moving over him as she whispered, 'Let me touch you . . . let me make love to you . . .'

Mark stared down at her, sweat sheening his skin as her fingers sought and found him and he gave a long, low strangled cry of pleasure, then closed his eyes, drawing ragged breaths as she stroked him, staring at him in a longing to show her love physically, make love to the man, give him everything she possibly could that would pleasure him...

He bent his head suddenly, kissing her fiercely, and his hands stripped her until they were both naked, sliding together, their limbs tangling, and the excitement was so fierce that Caroline was aware of a blood-beat in her body of such violent frenzy that it could only explode, shatteringly, soon, very soon...

'I love you!' Mark bit out thickly, and she felt the thrust of him sliding inside her as his fingers gripped her tighter and he moaned hoarsely, 'Oh, God, Caro...I love you like crazy...'

She cried out in agonised pleasure as their bodies merged, and suddenly he was moving against her, possessing her utterly, filling her with that heavy maleness, completely her master, driving into her again and again, his face dark red with desire, eyes glittering, breath coming in harsh, rapid gasps and she felt the excitement explode, sending her spasming all the way back down through that build-up of exquisite tension, clutching blindly at him as her body found hot, wet liberty impaled on his, and she heard his groans of disbelieving pleasure as he watched her face contorting and her body writhing, until his body was catapulted into violent ecstasy and it was her turn to watch.

Later, he said against her damp throat, 'Now I know why I was so overwhelmingly attracted to you. I must have been in love with you from the very beginning.' He lifted his head, sweat on his lashes. 'I just didn't re-

cognise it. Didn't want to. I've hated the thought of love
and marriage all my life. I was bound to kick and punch
it when I met it.'

Caroline laughed huskily, stroking his sweat-gleaming
throat. 'And I've always hated the very men I'm sexually attracted to. It's . . . it's about as close as you can
get to another person—isn't it?'

He smiled. 'Yes . . .' Then jealousy blazed in his eyes.
'What do you mean? You've felt this way before? About
other men?'

'Not like this,' she reassured him huskily. 'Never like
this. But I have occasionally met men I felt an attraction
to and I've always avoided them like the plague.'

'What does that make me?' he drawled wryly.

'It makes you the one who changed me forever.'

His black lashes flickered. 'Did you really never want
to make love with Stephen Daly?' he asked, a trace of
savage jealousy in his voice.

'I didn't even want to kiss him,' she confessed with a
sigh. 'To be honest, I think I started to get involved with
him as an escape from my feelings for you. I was so
aware of you, Mark, so intensely excited by you every
time I saw you . . .'

He smiled and kissed her mouth lingeringly. 'The
minute I saw you put that swine's ring on your finger
at the Ritz . . .' He shook his dark head, eyes wry. 'My
God, I felt waves of the most intense jealousy. I can
remember looking across the restaurant at you and
wanting to kill you, to kill you both. I felt like a savage.
How I controlled myself, I'll never know.'

'You were rather savage that night,' she said softly,
watching him through her lashes.

'I went home and raged for hours, trying to tell myself
I didn't give a damn what you did or whether I never

saw you again in my life, but of course I did. I cared far too much. I'd been after you for months, and suddenly I knew I had to have you, no matter what the cost. That's when I came up with that plan. To get you to Cornwall, make you admit you wanted me to make love to you, and then offer to make you my mistress.'

Her eyes narrowed. 'Yes, I was very offended by that offer.'

'I know,' he drawled with a grimace. 'It was stupid of me. I knew perfectly well you weren't my usual type of woman. Ladies like Venetia Blake and her predecessors were only too eager to go to bed with me. I didn't have to offer them apartments or fast cars, although I did occasionally buy them diamonds and——'

'Stop it,' she said thickly, her hands tightening on his broad shoulders. 'I don't want to hear about it, Mark! My God, what do you think I'm made of? Stone?'

'I'm trying to explain how——'

Angrily, she pushed away from him, saying hoarsely, 'I'm jealous of them! All of them! Any woman who's made love to you before is a threat because I did this out of love, and I believed you did it out of love and I can't tolerate the thought of——'

'Darling,' he said deeply, holding her, pushing her face into his damp throat where a pulse still beat, 'you have no need to be jealous of any of them. I didn't love them. I just wanted to go to bed with them.'

'Was Venetia your mistress?' she asked thickly, pain flooding her in waves.

'No,' he said wryly, and drew back to look at her in silence for a moment before saying thickly, 'Caroline, I hate to have to admit it, but I haven't been able to look at another woman since the day you walked into my office.'

She watched him jealously through her lashes. 'Is that the truth? Or are you just trying to make me feel better?'

'It's the truth,' he said deeply. 'You rammed into my bloodstream from that first day, and no other woman has attracted me since. I kept Venetia hanging around for a number of reasons, mainly because I've been a complete bastard with women all my life. But also because I couldn't bring myself to admit I felt so much for you.'

'Poor Venetia . . .' she said with a pained frown.

'Don't feel too much compassion for her,' he drawled wryly. 'She's in love with a French count who just married a film star and left Venetia without a backward glance. I didn't hurt her by keeping her around. In fact, I probably helped her get over the count.'

Caroline studied his hard, handsome face. Love washed over her in waves so strong that she suddenly felt weak with it, her eyes moving over her lover, her love, her soulmate.

'I remember the day I first looked into your eyes,' she said huskily. 'I remember it so clearly. That instant recognition . . .'

He smiled slowly, saying deeply, 'My twin soul. But we're in such different bodies, my love.'

'I suppose,' she said softly, 'that's why we're built to blend.'

He kissed her mouth lingeringly. 'You will blend with me forever, won't you? Marry me, I mean. I'm sorry it wasn't a serious proposal when it came, but I was desperate to stop you leaving me, leaving the firm. I was so heavily in love with you and I had to hold fast to the belief that it had happened to you, too, in that snow-bound cottage. I couldn't let myself believe for one second that you had felt nothing. I would just have died of the pain...'

'Of course I'll marry you,' she said huskily, kissing him. 'But only because it's the way it's done.'

'No white dress or orange blossom?' he teased.

'They're irrelevant,' she said softly, love filling her. 'All that's important is your soul and mine twinned together forever. Marrying you is just a way of announcing that joint love to the rest of the world.'

He smiled. 'Funny how everything changes when you fall in love. The oddest things suddenly make sense.'

She laughed and kissed him, burying her face in his neck.

He stroked her hair tenderly. 'We could have children, too...' he said carefully.

She felt even weaker with love. 'Oh, darling, yes. Children...'

He expelled his breath unsteadily. 'Thank God for that! I was afraid for one minute you would tell me your feelings about children had changed and you wanted to wait—or, worse, not have any at all.'

She raised her head to look at him. 'No, Mark. My feelings about children have changed—but it's a deepening, not a reversal, like the way I feel about marriage.' A smile touched her mouth and she said softly, 'I see children as creative lovemaking now. Our souls and bodies in a magic fusion that creates life.'

'Darling,' he said unsteadily, his eyes darkening, 'let's make life.'

And they did.

Accept 4 FREE Romances and 2 FREE gifts

Mills & Boon

FROM READER SERVICE

An irresistible invitation from Mills & Boon Reader Service. Please accept our offer of 4 free Romances, a CUDDLY TEDDY and a special MYSTERY GIFT... Then, if you choose, go on to enjoy 6 captivating Romances every month for just £1.70 each, postage and packing free. Plus our FREE Newsletter with author news, competitions and much more.

Send the coupon below to:
Reader Service, FREEPOST,
PO Box 236, Croydon,
Surrey CR9 9EL.

NO STAMP REQUIRED

Yes! Please rush me 4 Free Romances and 2 free gifts! Please also reserve me a Reader Service Subscription. If I decide to subscribe I can look forward to receiving 6 brand new Romances each month for just £10.20, post and packing free.

If I choose not to subscribe I shall write to you within 10 days - I can keep the books and gifts whatever I decide. I may cancel or suspend my subscription at any time. I am over 18 years of age.

Ms/Mrs/Miss/Mr ———————————————————— EP30R

Address ————————————————————————

————————————————————————————————

Postcode —————————— Signature ——————————

mps MAILING PREFERENCE SERVICE

Next Month's Romances

Each month you can choose from a wide variety of romance with Mills & Boon. Below are the new titles to look out for next month, why not ask either Mills & Boon Reader Service or your Newsagent to reserve you a copy of the titles you want to buy — just tick the titles you would like and either post to Reader Service or take it to any Newsagent and ask them to order your books.

Please save me the following titles:	Please tick	√
A DANGEROUS LOVER	Lindsay Armstrong	
RELUCTANT CAPTIVE	Helen Bianchin	
SAVAGE OBSESSION	Diana Hamilton	
TUG OF LOVE	Penny Jordan	
YESTERDAY'S AFFAIR	Sally wentworth	
RECKLESS DECEPTION	Angela Wells	
ISLAND OF LOVE	Rosemary Hammond	
NAIVE AWAKENING	Cathy Williams	
CRUEL CONSPIRACY	Helen Brooks	
FESTIVAL SUMMER	Charlotte Lamb	
AFTER THE HONEYMOON	Alexandra Scott	
THE THREAD OF LOVE	Anne Beaumont	
SECRETS OF THE NIGHT	Joanna Mansell	
RELUCTANT SURRENDER	Jenny Cartwright	
SUMMER'S VINTAGE	Gloria Bevan	
RITES OF LOVE	Rebecca Winters	

If you would like to order these books in addition to your regular subscription from Mills & Boon Reader Service please send £1.70 per title to: Mills & Boon Reader Service, P.O. Box 236, Croydon, Surrey, CR9 3RU, quote your Subscriber No:...
(If applicable) and complete the name and address details below. Alternatively, these books are available from many local Newsagents including W.H.Smith, J.Menzies, Martins and other paperback stockists from 8th January 1993.

Name:...

Address:...

....Post Code:............................

To Retailer: If you would like to stock M&B books please contact your regular book/magazine wholesaler for details.

You may be mailed with offers from other reputable companies as a result of this application.
If you would rather not take advantage of these opportunities please tick box ☐